MADMAN'S MEMORY

MADMAN'S MEMORY

by Roger Vercel

TRANSLATED FROM THE FRENCH BY

Warre Bradley Wells

RANDOM HOUSE · NEW YORK

TO YVES BERTHELOT

MADMAN'S MEMORY

FRANÇOISE was driving fast in the flat
country. The road ran straight toward
a dark mass of tall trees bounded by a
low wall. Out of this wall the entrance
to the estate carved a green rectangle. The car passed through
the gateway and was submerged in an avenue of old beeches
with light trunks. At its end, flanked by a sequoia and a cedar,
behind a flower-bed with tulips already coming into leaf like
lance-heads, rose the wide front of Plangomeur, with two
square turrets jutting out, capped by three-cornered copings.
From its steep roof soared high, narrow chimneys, compact
and slim as masts. The house itself gave the impression, at
once portly and proud, of a frigate. Its windows, all alike,
matched with the precision of portholes.

Plangomeur was one of the finest Saint-Malo style houses
in the Rance valley, and it bore the mark of Garangeau. Le
Nôtre himself had laid out its three-terraced garden in its
setting of marshland. La Hourie, the famous Saint-Malo
privateer, the man who stained his face and hands blood-red
before his attacks, had it built for him in 1714, the same year
in which he carried Tortola in the Virgin Islands by assault.

As soon as he came home, enriched by his exploit, he had
looked around, like all corsairs, for some shady, obscure spot
in his native countryside, where he might brood over his board-
ings and display his silver plate and his golden ewers, on which
he had chiselled, with his own hand, the arms and mottoes of
conquered commodores. Other corsairs of his time secluded
themselves in trees and ivy and raised doves. Among their

malouinières, so-called because their architects had repro-
duced the square, sturdy style, the triangular roofs and the
monumental chimneys of Saint-Malo, one might be called
"Florida" or another "Sea Vale," depending upon which the
corsairs felt more keenly when they built them: their pride in
the past or their serenity in the present. But La Hourie had
scorned the name of his conquest for his house. He had kept
the name that belonged to the ground on which he built it. But
it was said that, as had been done before in the case of Solidor,
he had mixed the foundations of Plangomeur with ox-blood.

Françoise got out of her car in front of the outhouses, where
a stable had been turned into a garage. A gardener was busy
training rambler roses along a wall. He took the strips of raffia,
which looked like an untrimmed mustache, out of his mouth,
and said, "Madame is expecting Madame."

Then he screwed up his eyes in his broad, red face, and
added, "She's waiting for you in her bedroom."

He was an old Newfoundland fisherman who lost his bearings as soon as he embarked on the third person. Françoise
looked at the stems, already swelling with sap, which lay
tangled on the ground.

"That's the fine work of that nor'west blow last night," said
the gardener. "My word, it can't have been much fun off
Cézembre for the boats waiting for the floodtide. I'm told that
the *Marie-Yonnik* had to put back to port. That's a thing that
happened to me only once in all my twenty-two trips."

Françoise knew that he was inexhaustible once he got under
way talking about the Banks. She turned aside, pointing to the
roses.

"Luckily they haven't suffered too much."

"They're *Gloria Mundi.* They grow like weeds."

Françoise went along the path, a granite path precisely the

same as the gray granite of the house, and turned through the central door into a paneled hall, out of which rose a wide oak staircase. Its banisters were made from the beams of one of the corsair's brigantines. As Françoise ascended it, browned seascapes kept her company along the wall. The smoke of their cannon-shot was turning into tar, blackening their ships. At the mast-heads streamed, still in full splendor, the blue bunting with its white cross of the corsairs of Saint-Malo.

Françoise walked a short way down a long corridor lined with suits of armor and knocked at a high door, adorned with that red ship, carved in the round, which was to be found on all the paneling in Plangomeur. She opened the door. From the threshold of the spacious room crowded with chairs, tables and brackets and broken up by screens, she looked around for its occupant. A pudgy hand stuck up from a Louis XVI armchair and beckoned her.

"Good day, Mamma," said Françoise.

Madame la Hourie gave her the tips of her fingers.

"Why, what have you been doing?" she asked. "I was getting anxious about you. You know very well that I can't stand waiting nowadays."

"I went down to the river on my way back," Françoise explained, "to see Jégu about those two boatloads of gravel."

"And is he going to send them?"

"He wasn't there."

"Naturally! Did you have any damage at Le Fraô?"

"Not much."

Madame la Hourie looked at her with a reproachful air.

"People always say 'Not much,' and then, when you get the bill, you get a shock too. Did you go to see the carpenter?"

"No. Marie-Ange is going."

5

"Your tenant? Then, of course, they'll get together and cheat you. You're not very businesslike, my girl."

Madame la Hourie shivered.

"Oh, you didn't shut the door!" she exclaimed.

"Yes, I did."

"I'm frozen, anyway."

She leaned forward for a moment toward the big, bright fire that danced in the high marble fireplace. Her thick, flabby body looked all the more bulky in her swansdown-lined coat, swelling out at her stomach and her knees. Then she lay back again in her chair, her thin gray hair leaning against it, her stumpy, swollen hands clasping its arms. She closed her heavy-lidded eyes. Françoise gazed for a moment at her yellow face, her lax jowls, her thick, purplish lips. Then she asked, "Are you in pain?"

Madame la Hourie opened her eyes again and stared at Françoise. Once more Françoise reproached herself over the sense of repulsion that stare made her feel. Those eyes, those big blue eyes, glassy, almost opaque despite their color, watched her with pitiless curiosity. Behind their dim veil she could sense the passage of a whole throng of intense emotions: spite or anger, disdain or mockery, distrust or aversion. But never a gleam flickered in them. They simply hardened, as though their watery murk had just congealed. Then, suddenly, the eyes slid away, for fear lest they betray their ambush.

Once she had stopped staring at Françoise, Madame la Hourie, as usual, seemed seized with embarrassment. She arranged the folds over her knees with fussy little movements, following them with her eyes, all at once alive.

"I'm not in pain," she replied, speaking very quickly, "or, at least, not more than usual."

6

She nodded, backward and forward, by way of denial. "No, not more than usual."

The motion of her head, the wrong way, was disconcerting.

The silence dragged. Madame la Hourie seemed absent-minded. Sitting still, her hands folded in her lap, she fixed her big eyes on a ray of sunlight on the back of a chair.

Still standing, Françoise said, in her level voice, "Grioul told me you were asking for me."

"Grioul? Oh, yes!"

The words seemed to jerk the old lady out of her chair. A sudden heave of her squat body brought her to her feet. Once again Françoise was astonished that she should be at once so bulky and so nimble. Shaking herself, she slipped off the coat that padded her out, and her slack, shapeless body, its fat trembling in her black merino bodice, started moving with absurd liveliness. The old lady began to walk about nervously. Her fingers crumbled emptiness. Her lips formed soundless words. Her shoulders twitched as though she had an itch. The sway of her powerful hips could be seen through the thickness of her dress. This almost convulsive agitation, after her long inertia, was disturbing. It was as though someone had touched, by mistake, the lever which set a heavy automaton in motion.

After wandering about for some time, disarranging various things, Madame la Hourie finally picked up a large flat package lying on a sideboard. The string had already been removed, and she proceeded to unwrap it. As she bent over it, she seemed satisfied that she had reached her goal. A gloating smile creased the lower part of her fat face, crumpling her chins and becoming lost in them. Her pudgy fingers unfolded the wrapping paper with skillful speed. Françoise waited, on her guard.

7

From a last piece of tissue paper her mother-in-law took a large photograph surrounded by a flat border. She held it out at arms' length.

"Look at this!"

It was a very young man, standing with his left hand resting on the arm of a chair. His round face, almost without chin or cheekbones, was one of those soft faces that look as though they had been steeped in hot water, so flaccid and washed-out was the flesh. His glossy hair had a very straight parting. His eyes, very wide open for the occasion, stared with lordly stupidity at a point at which he had obviously been told to look. His concern about his pose threw into higher relief the stiffness of his body and the carriage of his head, raised too high.

Madame la Hourie went on holding the photograph at arms' length, and her smile, turning sentimental, made her lips tremble a little.

"Isn't it his living image?" she asked.

Françoise studied it.

"I've never seen that photo before," she replied.

"No, as a matter of fact, you don't know it. I—I found the print a fortnight ago, when I was clearing out a cupboard."

Françoise knew that her mother-in-law was lying. It happened so often that she had given up even trying to fathom these pretenses. For that matter, they were always so complicated, so tiring to work out, that it was simpler to seem taken in by them.

At last Madame la Hourie carefully laid the photo on a table. Then she picked up another package, still tied, and handed it to her daughter-in-law.

"This one is for you."

"Thank you."

An envelope tucked inside the package slid out and fell to

the floor. Françoise picked it up. Her fingers felt the hard thickness of cardboard.

"This is the print, I suppose?"

Madame la Hourie all but snatched it from her.

"Yes. Give it to me. We don't want it any more now."

She hastily thrust it into a drawer, which she shut and locked. Then she took a deep breath, as though she had just escaped some danger. As Françoise stared at her, she said very quickly,

"I wanted these enlargements for the fifth, you know. Barthé promised me them all right, but you know what photographers are. I had to go back three times. 'Monsieur Barthé,' I said to him . . ."

She broke off. It was in a different tone that she went on, "The fifth! It's just a year since the fifth. . . ."

It was just a year since her only son, Luc la Hourie, Françoise's husband, had been lost with one of his trawlers.

Françoise awaited the inevitable comment on the tragic date with that impassive deference which she showed toward all evocations of the dead man. But Madame la Hourie simply said, "Tell Grioul to hang it up for you. Take it with you."

Her daughter-in-law was at the door when she called her back.

"You know, my child, you'll have to go back about that gravel. I've been waiting for it for a month. Besides . . ."

"I'll put this in my room, and then I'll go."

In her room with its white sycamore furniture, chosen by her husband for its compact cosiness, Françoise opened a low chest of drawers. But, just as she was about to thrust the portrait into it, she changed her mind, tore off the white paper and looked at it.

It was strange that she did not know this photo of Luc, when she had had to submit over and over again to the exhibition of all the others, even those in which her husband's face was to be found among the faces of friends only with the aid of a magnifying glass. His too-wide-open eyes astonished her. He looked as though he were afraid. But why should he have been afraid? Hadn't his mother been with him, that day, the same as every other day, at the photographer's, the same as everywhere else?

She took the portrait in both hands, as her mother-in-law had done just now, and studied it with an unsparing scrutiny. Once again she found the nervous twitch, badly touched-up, at the corner of Luc's mouth; his Adam's apple, jutting out despite the fat neck; his prominent ears, with their over-large shells; the tension of his fingers flat on the arm of the chair. Subconsciously, she was making sure whether all his little blemishes, which had once disillusioned her one by one, but which she had refused to add up, were all to be seen.

Suddenly she became conscious of her insulting inspection. She felt ashamed of it, for she knew that, lacking regret, she owed the dead man indulgence and consideration. She thrust the portrait into a drawer.

Françoise had promised to go back to the Rance about that gravel. This morning, a run into le Mené about one of the farmhouse roofs that had been torn off by the storm; this afternoon, a trip to the river. Not for a long time had she known such a busy day! She laughed at the idea, mockingly, as she slammed the door of her car.

This time she found Jégu at his pit, amid piles of gravel. He apologized for the delay and promised to send the gravel to Plangomeur the next day. Leaving her car behind, Françoise climbed a steep path which came out on top of the cliffs and went forward to the edge.

In front of her, a wide stretch of blue sea, the tidal Rance streamed eastward between hills in a swift, smooth flow. An eddy swirled now and again at its banks along the walls of rock. The tide flowed up the river in long, sleek, shining sweeps, curving in the distance at the edges of the sandbanks which it had already submerged.

The silence of the strong flood was impressive. There was not a murmur, not a lapping. The water ran like oil, without a check at the rim of the reefs which it overran. But there was a sudden gust of wind, and Françoise had to snatch at her scarf as it blew away.

The wind, like the water, came from the west. That way the Rance opened out in a superb, shimmering reach toward the sea. Its silvery flood flowed between banks where the tawny rocks were crowned with woods already in leaf with the early spring. Soft stretches of greensward ran down to its banks between avenues of tall trees. A broad band of sunlight shone between the cliffs, and black-headed gulls came in gaily with the boats that surrendered themselves to the tide, using neither sails nor oars.

But Françoise turned her back on the pale sea and gazed upstream. As though carried away by the impetuous return of the flood, her memories and her thoughts went with it strongly toward the sources of the river, where she had played and dreamed and cried as a child.

There, beside the old road to Collinée, a spring issued out of broken rock. A trickle of water escaped from a toad-hole on a farm or tumbled between the stones of a sunken lane. Françoise remembered sloping meadows dripping into brooks, twisted stumps of trees weeping into them, peat-bogs oozing black bubbles. She remembered all the sources of the river in that countryside streaming with water.

She had gone back this very morning to that wild land of

woods, that Mené which long haunted her once she saw it again.

Its sparse cultivation dotted the chilly soil formed from the decomposition of schist. Its clayey fields, drained by parallel ditches, were bordered by steep slopes on which grew the twisted pollard-oaks, stumpy and gnarled, of the Gallo region. Its villages—church, schoolhouse *cum* municipal building, grocery *cum* tobacconist *cum* inn—were nothing more in summer than dried kernels in the red dust. Its peasants bore strange names of savage tribes: the "Black Necks" at Saint-Launeuc, the "Foxes" at Trébry, the "Toads" at Plessala, and, at Mérillac, the "Hornet Heads," from the name of those knotty knobs like warts on oaks. Here and there gleamed livid ponds, flush with their banks, and the hamlets beside them bore names that meant Mire, Heath or Scrub.

The manor house in which Françoise was born and brought up was called Le Fraô, from the Breton name of those thieving crows which hemmed it in all winter. The house seemed to have escaped from the forest, from Hardouinais Wood, one of the steepest stretches of the legendary Forest of Brocéliande. It lay along the threshold of the forest, and yew-trees nibbled at it to half its height. On stormy days it was lashed by oaks whose roots had raised its lower floors. To the south, on its sunny side, ran the Upper Rance.

For years Françoise had looked down at the river with longing, because it was the one bright thing in the somber landscape. Later, she had followed her father there when he fished for trout. On its banks she had chased flies and grasshoppers and hunted for eels under the warm stones. Her elder sister, Hélène, taught her to tuck up her skirt and let an icy ring of water rise slowly up her thighs.

When the foundered fisherman, gaitered with mud and scratched by briars, uncoupled his rods ready to return home,

12

Françoise used to gaze at the stream and ask, "Where does the river go?"

Bent, dragging his heavy boots, the old fisherman growled, "A long way off. . . . Come on!"

Françoise followed him back to the dark, dull house. Her elder sister, for her part, fled from it and vanished for whole days when their father was shooting or fishing.

The north front of Le Fraô bristled with turrets: a ridiculous effort of masonry to achieve architecture. It was, so to speak, a symbol of ambitions without means, of the vain regrets which were shut up in it. Comte Achard had taught his daughters that his wretched idleness was a privilege of birth, an aspect of honor. For endless hours Françoise had repeated the "roll-call," that awful list of ancestors, always apt to be demanded.

"Tudual, Herbert du Fraô de Lanhéac, 1146-1213.

"Olivier, Tanneguy du Fraô de Lanhéac, Lord of Miniac and of Marcé in Normandy, 1178-1251 . . ."

At the slightest mistake, her father shouted "No!" with such violence that it made her tremble.

She remembered her father as having always been old. She could still see him driving away mushroom pickers who ventured into his woods, his oaths ending in wheezes, his cheeks suddenly blotched. There were whispers that he fired at poachers with buckshot. At Le Fraô, he might sit for hours before the fire, his legs stretched out as though to forbid his daughters even the idea of climbing onto his knees. He wore a velvet hunting jacket, with bronze buttons on which wolves showed their claws. His silence was so forbidding that farmers who came to ask for repairs or postponement of rent stammered in his presence. At the time of the inventory of churches, he went to Dinan to put up a fight, and spent two days in the Republican jail.

Still, Françoise had suddenly come to love him that day when, now that she was old enough to know how children are born, her aunt told her, "Your father has not yet forgiven you because you cost him your mother's life."

Never did Françoise listen to him so closely as when he talked to her on the banks of the Rance. He was a bard and a member of several archeological societies; he had been working as long as she could remember on a *History of Political Crimes in Upper Brittany;* and he knew enough about the Rance to fill its whole course with blood.

Upstream from Le Fraô, the Rance ran past Lanrelas. Françoise loved the village for its chapels, squat as haystacks, where Saint Gilles cured fear and Saint Georges cured swine-fever in pigs and impetigo in children. She loved it for its little fountain, its vault washed with bluish chalk, whose water relieved colic after a prayer to Saint Fiacre. The Rance left Lanrelas by way of a green valley, passed and repassed under a new road, and curved around huge flat stones, hollowed out into polished basins.

One day Achard du Fraô had found Françoise there.

"Lanrelas?" he replied, in answer to her question. "It means 'the Place of Slaughter.' "

Pitilessly he described to his daughter how victims had their throats cut by the Druids on the Stone of the Giant. He made her run her finger along the groove in the stone where the blood had flowed.

One evening, he had taken her to Bosquen, to the edge of a plateau on which some ruins crumbled away, buried in brakes and landslides. From here you could see the Rance curving between poplars. But her father had turned her away from the river, and told her the story of the death-agony of Gilles de Bretagne. Beneath these ruins he had screamed with hunger,

14

vomited poisoned soup and, finally, during the night of April 25, 1450, died stifled beneath the buttocks of two Huguenot cavalrymen, "Oreille-Pelue" and "Maletouche," one sitting on his chest, the other on his mouth. His nostrils and his ears had been stuffed with wax to keep in the blood and suggest a natural death. His body had been carried across the Rance on the shoulders of the monks of Bosquen, at the very spot where Françoise and her father had crossed it.

Achard enthused about this fine crime, so long premeditated, so cleverly concealed. But for night after night, trembling terribly, Françoise struggled against the buttocks of old soldiers crushing her chest.

Of all the sinister dead who hemmed her in at Le Fraô, however, it was "the little girl" who haunted her the longest.

One stifling August afternoon, her father gravely took off his hat on top of a bare hill. She could still see the sweep with which he did it, his thin hair stuck to his head in narrow strands by sweat.

"This," he said, "is Saint-Réjant. It was from here that *he* set off."

Then, in his hoarse voice, which became a bark when he got excited, he told Françoise the story of Robinault de Saint-Réjant, a relative of theirs. During Christmas night in the year 1800, Robinault stopped the wheeled cask which he was driving in the rue Saint-Nicaise in Paris, and tossed the horse's reins to a little girl who happened to be passing. It was only by a minute's margin that Bonaparte's carriage missed being blown to pieces by Robinault's infernal machine. A gunnery officer in the Royal Navy, he had contrived it cleverly in the form of a huge box of grapeshot, but the fuse was a little too long.

As he recalled this error in calculation, more than a century back, Achard du Fraô's lips turned down with disappointment.

"And what happened to the little girl?" asked Françoise.

Her father shrugged his shoulders. When she burst into tears, he scolded her, and told her not to be a fool.

That night, when it was time for her to go to bed, the stubborn child who had clenched her teeth on her terror for months, broke down. Shrieking, she flung herself against the wall in a panic. The servant, Maclovie, a half-wit with a face like a Negress, calmly reproached her.

"What's all the fuss about, you big cry-baby? Are you afraid of the night? What's the difference between the night and the day?"

All at once, Françoise stopped crying. It was then that she made up her mind not to fear the dead, to open her eyes wide in the dark, and not hide her head under the bedclothes any more.

About this time, her aunt Angélique, her father's sister-in-law, came to Le Fraô to hear about the progress of the *History of Political Crimes*, in which she was collaborating. She had graduated in literature and prided herself upon having been a pupil of Abbé Duchesne at the Carmelite convent. While resting between chapters, she was dumbfounded to learn about the world of horrors in which her niece had been struggling. She stormed at her brother-in-law, in that way of hers which terrorized the whole family, called him a barbarian, and promptly took Françoise off to Caulnes, where she put her into the Mathieu Ory Seminary.

The school, with its balustraded terrace and its wooded gardens, lay alongside the Rance. It was a Louis XVI chateau, and its purchase and furnishing had originally run the community so far into debt that, as Aunt Angélique put it, "If it

16

had been a question of laity, it would border on passing a worthless check; but, as they are nuns, one can only call it trust in Providence."

The seminary prided itself on bearing the name of a son of Caulnes, a preaching friar who had been Grand Inquisitor of France under Françoise I and Henri II. A suspect book by a Spaniard, Inigo, from the province of Guipúzcoa, had been referred to his tribunal. The author had barely escaped being ceremonially whipped at the Sainte-Barbe College. But Mathieu Ory had approved his *Spiritual Exercises,* and defended Ignatius de Loyola and his Society before the King and the Pope. The sisters were proud of the fact.

"You must always remember, my children," they would tell their pupils, "that it was to a Breton, to a son of Caulnes, that we owe the Society of Jesus."

Here Françoise served an enforced apprenticeship in peace. At first she was tense, silent, slit-eyed, and refused to eat, like all free young animals when they are caged. Then she suddenly surrendered when she realized that she had been shut up by way of a privilege, by way of isolating her from the masses, by way of "bringing her up." She felt the full meaning of the phrase. Once at her ease, she found a sensuous pleasure in the security of the convent, just as on stormy days you feel the shelter of a room close about you. The neighboring peasants of la Chapelle-Blanche, it was said, walled up the windows when they were given new houses. Françoise thought they were quite right. The inside was something to be defended against the outside.

The nuns, too, young and old, had a sense of living in a citadel. They had had to canvass and beg, to suffer remonstrance and refusal for so long that all of them had acquired a contempt for the outside world. This contempt was peculiarly active, because it came not so much from their novices' education as from their personal grievances. Now that at length the convent was paid for to the very last bill, they enjoyed the serenity of its rule and the pleasure of a future precisely foreseen. But with that experience of women, whoever they may be, who have learned to know men well through having to ask them for money, they were quite capable of combating curiosity and desire among their pupils. Content with their hard-won position, they hated looking farther afield. Even the Mother Superior, in her science classes, used to reply curtly, "That is one of God's secrets," whenever a pupil asked a question that burrowed beyond the text-book explanation.

The piety which the nuns required was healthy and reasonable, inimical to emotional outbursts, and firmly based upon daily duties. Their Breton strength of will made them like iron toward slackness and softness. But one day, when Françoise cut her chin to the bone on a stone, and bore the stitching of the wound without flinching, Mother Saint-Alban stroked her hair. Her show of affection astonished the convent even more than the patient's endurance.

One evening, the Mother Superior summoned Françoise to her well-polished study which smelled of yellow wax.

"My child," she said, "you must say many a prayer for your sister."

Then, without seeming to notice that Françoise had turned pale, still looking her straight in the eyes, she added, "For her soul."

"Is she dead?" asked Françoise.

Mother Saint-Alban bowed her head. She did so in the same way as when she grudgingly granted leave. She seemed to be conceding this death. . . .

18

At Le Fraô, Françoise found only Maclovie, busy peeling vegetables at the dead girl's bedside, since there was no one else to keep the death-watch and attend to the cooking. When Françoise started to lift the sheet drawn over her sister's face, the old woman stopped her, grasping her wrist in her bony fingers.

"You mustn't do that!" she exclaimed. "If you lift it, she'll follow you all your life. The dead always do." Then she went on, "She was killed. They found her last night in the mill pool. Her hair was all tangled in the roots."

"On purpose?" breathed Françoise.

Maclovie shrugged her shoulders.

"Why, of course! She'd sinned, the hussy. Monsieur turned her out of the house."

A wild wave of pity drove Françoise to her father's closed door. There she cried, shouted, stormed. Maclovie called her back.

"You won't get him to come out. He said he'd never see her again, dead or alive. Be quiet! You mustn't make a noise like that when there's death in the house."

Tottering, Françoise went back to Hélène's body. The sheet had slipped, and she could see a bit of her blue brow, a strand of her dank hair.

"Haven't you got your rosary?" asked Maclovie.

But Françoise could not even pray. First of all, she wanted to understand. Hélène had "sinned," and Françoise knew just what that meant: a lover, and then a child coming. The girls of the countryside, from daughters of manors to cow-herds, knew all about this sin and talked about it without hypocrisy as a danger. A revered veil was kept in the parish church, a tulle veil which the church guild lent to the Children of Mary for their weddings. But sometimes the committee refused it. In that stern village, misconduct was thus publicly proclaimed and punished. Some guilty girls defied the stigma. Others left the district. But there had been some, before Hélène, driven mad with shame, who had gone straight to the river or the pool.

That night, Françoise had passed judgment, just as the village had done; for the body beneath the sheet betrayed love with all the imperious shamelessness of the dead, who no longer keep up appearances or lend themselves to the prudence of the living. Since Hélène had loved, tempestuous, eager Hélène, love could not be that rosy sentiment described in the church-guild novels. Hélène could have been driven to the Rance only by that wild force, that vile madness, which seized upon farm beasts in the spring.

Once she realized this, Françoise fiercely agreed with her elder sister's refusal to survive her shame.

At midnight, Maclovie said, "It was that young Braud. He came to tell your father that he was quite ready to marry her. Monsieur broke his dog-whip over his back. A common quarryman! He had a bad time of it, the boor. Monsieur did quite right."

Françoise nodded her head slowly in agreement. Yes, Comte du Fraô had done quite right to drive the yokel away with his dog-whip.

After Hélène's funeral, their father unbarred his door and said to Françoise, "You're not going back to Caulnes. Your place is here."

He added, "See that nothing of hers is left in the house."

For weeks, the two of them tracked down the dead girl to clear all traces of her from Le Fraô. Françoise devoted herself to the task with inflexible sternness, burning letters and photos and sending clothes to distant orphanages, whence there was

20

no chance of seeing them come back on little girls.

One evening, she went to the Brauds' home and told the old man, "If my father meets your son, he'll kill him."

"Not likely!" sneered the Braud. "We're not living in the days of the seigneurs any more."

All the same, young Braud left the district the next week.

Françoise conceded nothing to her dead sister except prayers. Unknown to her father, she had a weekly mass said for Hélène for a year. She sold a gold chain to pay for them.

One day, without any previous sign of his decision, Achard du Fraô announced, "We're leaving here."

The next day but one, at dawn, the three of them drove down the valley and Françoise's father pulled up in front of that high house whose gable she could now see above the roofs of Le Minihic. It had belonged to her mother. It had its foundations in the slime of the Rance, a slime that was not mud, but silver-gray clay veined with blue threads which shone in the sun. In this plastic slime the swirls and eddies of the flood-tide wrote arabesques that Françoise learned to know by heart. The house was an old mill, with an array of narrow windows facing the Rance, but it looked like a monastery, because it had denied itself cornices, corbels or any other projection toward the outside world.

Here the ebb and flow of the tide measured endless days for Françoise. At the flow, the sea rose right to the walls, and sailing boats went by. Then, at the ebb, after the water's great retreat, the Rance became a broken plain of tawny sand, in which blue streams trickled and little bent figures were busy looking for shell-fish. With Maclovie for chaperone, Françoise went fishing again. When she came home in the evening, her lips tasted of salt.

But the door of the mill soon closed upon her. Six months

21

after their arrival on the little flat-stoned mole, her father was struck down by an attack of cerebral hemorrhage. For five years she stayed at the semi-paralyzed man's bedside, watching the twitching of his distorted face, listening to the stammering of his deformed lips. They were five terrible years, devoted to her half-dead father, who spent day and night in a dreadful struggle against the useless part of his body, filling his big bedroom with incoherent curses, making movements which he could not complete. Françoise did her utmost for her fierce patient, never flinching, even when he aimed clumsy blows at her.

At the same time she had to renew the contest against her dead sister; for the image of Hélène invaded her father's disordered mind and wrought havoc in it. His twisted mouth kept muttering words of remorse, and this she had to overcome. She devoted herself to the task with a passionate persistence which discarded not a jot of her former pride. She recalled the indignant contempt she had felt at Le Fraô, and insisted that her father had done his duty in driving his fallen daughter from home and whipping her seducer. Justice must be upheld! One night, for some minutes, the old man tried to speak his elder daughter's name, stressing its two syllables in breathless efforts: "Hell-Henn, Hell-Henn." Then Françoise found courage to bid him be quiet, and with such authority that Comte Achard fell silent.

When she had at last seen him go in a peaceful death, Françoise found herself for the first time without duties, without struggles, mistress of her own life. Her aunt, who lived in a pleasant house buried in trees on the other side of the river, had offered to share it with her. But Françoise preferred her mill, old Maclovie's grumbling devotion, and, above all, her happy torpor of convalescence, which sometimes made her

22

smile to herself. She felt as though she had contracted not only an illness, but also her father's old age at his bedside, and that she would now be cured of both.

One summer afternoon, a young man out for a stroll followed her along the cliff path, pestering her with extravagant compliments. He sang the praises of her hair, her figure, her walk. He complained because he could not see her face and her eyes. He begged her to turn round. He pursued her all the way home.

His attentions were the signal for new struggles for Françoise. Aroused by the desire of this stranger, her starved, youthful instincts stirred deep within her. To master them took all her faith, her pride, above all the sense of horror which Hélène's breach of honor had left in her. After months of fighting and prayer, she all but accepted the fate of many well-born, but poor girls—to grow old alone in the midst of good works, without love, without children.

And then one evening, on the very bank of this river . . .

Françoise walked away from the cliff. She brushed that memory aside. She had had too much of it.

In front of the gravel merchant's low house her car awaited her. She got in and drove off again. At the first crossroad, she did not take the main road to Saint-Servan but a side-road which wound its way amid fields of cabbage and beetroot: spacious fields in which short rows of trees stood guard here and there.

Suddenly, rounding a bend, she had to stop. A concrete pole lay across the road. Men were busy around a truck carrying a winch. One of them left the group and walked toward the car. He was the only one bareheaded; all the others were wearing caps. As soon as she realized that he was approaching to speak to her, Françoise had a look at him. He wore a leather jacket

23

and gaiters, and he was tall and broad-shouldered. He had a strong face, a high forehead, firm, red lips. His bold brown eyes sought her through the haze on the windshield. When he reached the door, he bent forward and said,

"I'm sorry, Mademoiselle. You'll have to wait about five minutes."

Françoise had only half-lowered the window. She nodded. The man straightened himself and set off again toward the workmen. Then he turned round, glanced at the car's wheels, came back, and bent forward at the door once more.

"Your left front wheel is punctured, Mademoiselle," he said.

Françoise got out and stood beside him, looking at the tire, which whistled as it flattened.

"It will keep going so long as you're driving," remarked the man, "but once you stop, it goes flat very fast."

Françoise took off her coat and hat and laid them on the seat. She shook her bare head, and her chestnut hair, now free, fluffed up. Then she went to the tool chest and took out the jack and a spanner.

Squatting down, she attacked one bolt, which turned easily. But the next held fast, despite all the power of her arm which stretched the black silk of her blouse back and forth. It was not till then that the man lent a hand.

"Allow me," he said. "They usually screw them on like mad in a garage."

With one heave, he got the bolt to turn, and then he quickly unscrewed the others. Françoise put the jack under the axle. He took the handle from her, raised the car, took off the muddy wheel and adjusted the spare. As he stood up again, he rubbed his muddy hands against each other.

24

"I'm so sorry," exclaimed Françoise. "You've got yourself all dirty."

"Well, you haven't spoiled your gloves," he laughed, "so that's something."

When Françoise thanked him, he went on, "It was my fault, because I stopped you. But for that, you'd have got to the next garage. You'll find one two kilometers away."

He looked at the concrete pole, which the workmen had just fixed to steel cables attached to the winch.

"You'll be able to get on in a couple of minutes."

He took a few steps toward the workmen and shouted, "Hoist!"

Gears creaked, the cables tautened, and the post rose slowly. The men guided it with ropes. Standing still, his hands in the pockets of his leather jacket, the foreman shouted at them again, roughly, "Look out there! Pull to the left!"

When the post was standing in its hole, he nodded approval curtly and came back to Françoise. She had put on her coat and hat again. He stared at her with a surprise which he took no trouble to hide. Now that her head was covered, she looked quite different. Her thick hair had disappeared beneath her hat, and so had her wide, young forehead. There was a vague look of distrust in her green eyes, enlarged by the shadow of the felt brim. The set of her full lips betrayed half determination, half disappointment.

All at once, because he had been staring at her too long, she leaned forward and opened the door. Then, just as she was getting into the car, she turned around and asked, "Is this the line of posts that are going to cut across the grounds of Plangomeur?"

The man nodded.

"We're taking them down to the Rance, to give power to the mill," he replied. "Then we'll attack the stretch across Plangomeur. Does it belong to you?"

"It belongs to my mother-in-law."

Françoise had replied curtly, just as he had asked his question. But he broke into a laugh.

"Oh," he said, "she's the lady who's written us all those letters."

Françoise remembered those letters of protest over which her mother-in-law had spent a whole week. They were ridiculous, to be sure; but this laugh of his, which proclaimed the fact, irritated her.

"You can't expect her to thank you for wanting to make a mess of her grounds," she retorted.

She took her seat as she spoke. The man closed the door. The window was down, and he bent forward.

"We couldn't take the line anywhere else," he said. "We won't do more harm than we can help."

"It will be too much at best," replied Françoise.

She started the engine. The man was still holding onto the edge of the window. She stared at him, and her eyes hardened.

"Maybe," he muttered. "We fell trees, but we let in some light."

As though there was no more to be said, he let go of the car, straightened himself, and stepped back. Françoise did not look at him again. For a moment she hesitated, tempted to continue the skirmish. Then she decided that he was no more than a passerby and drove away.

THE dining room at Plangomeur had been planned by La Hourie for the sumptuous feasts which marked his return, when he could not regale his guests in the eating-houses of La Crevaille. It had witnessed some of those drinking bouts with which the adventurers took their revenge for their diet of bacon and water on board ship. It was said that the corsair had entertained Vauban there, when he came to design the forts of Saint-Malo, and that in it Duclos-Guyot, that squanderer of gold, had made piastres fly by heating them in a frying-pan and then throwing them out of the windows to little peasant boys, who burned their hands when they picked them up.

The sideboard had been carved out of captured ebony by a Lower Breton sculptor. La Hourie had brought him from Locronan, where he made oak linen-cupboards for the India Company. As though seized with madness at the sight of those huge blocks of precious wood, he had constructed a fantastic sideboard in three arcaded tiers, bristling with pinnacles. As for the massive table, it was more golden than an altar, for La Hourie had inlaid it with ornaments taken from the poop escutcheon of a Spanish galleon. Gilded balusters, once belonging to big Indiamen mounting fifty guns, lorded it all around the great room.

Two seascapes by Van Ostade filled the master panels. La Hourie had supervised their painting in person, to make sure that they were correct. Both of them represented the taking of Tortola: one, the naval engagement, in which the corsair's

27

three brigantines clung like horse flies to the English ships of the line; the other, the assault on the town by little figures in red kerchiefs who landed in indigo water up to their chests. At the end of the room, a full-length portrait of the corsair, painted by Rigaud, dominated the vast fireplace. It represented La Hourie in court costume and a full wig, his hand resting on a book—his memoirs.

Madame La Hourie and her daughter-in-law lunched on either side of the monumental table, whose dimensions did not dismay Françoise, inured as she was to isolation. The meal was served by a tight-lipped old servant, whose eyes knew their place. Her hair, under its square net, was still black.

Madame la Hourie ate very little, but, lest she should embarrass Françoise, she toyed with the food on her plate all through the meal. It was one of those little refinements of a well-brought-up woman which sometimes earns forgiveness for serious offenses.

When they came to the dessert, she asked, "Haven't you told Grioul to hang Luc's photo in your room?"

"Not yet," replied Françoise.

"Well, tell him."

A ray of sunlight suddenly struck La Hourie's portrait, and Françoise's eyes turned toward his face, instantly lit up. She was startled to notice, for the first time, how much the corsair resembled Luc, her husband, the man posed in the enlargement which her mother-in-law had just mentioned. There was the same roundness of face, the same narrowed mouth with its thick lower lip, the same dilated eyes, the same solemnity of attitude.

The likeness was so laughable that Françoise turned her eyes away again. She had been taught from childhood never to compare ancestors and descendants, to listen without visible scorn to the latter priding themselves on the former. The greater the difference between them, the less one should seem to be measuring it. This was a fundamental caste law, and she still respected it by instinct.

Now, during one of the usual long waits between courses, she gazed at the picture on the wall opposite her, the storming of Tortola, the little men in red kerchiefs struggling in the blue sea. At their head La Hourie raised his ax above parallel waves. She knew it was he, because he was alone and in front. Then, suddenly, she remembered that she had first seen Luc, too, up to his neck in water, his arms raised, just like his ancestor.

Once again she saw the river, one bright October afternoon, and the strange fisherman crossing the rocks below her. He cast his line into the eddies too slackly and fiddled endlessly with that irritating catch of his reel. Francoise turned her eyes away and looked upstream because he spoiled the broad, fine sweep of the water for her.

At the "plop" of his fall, she turned around again and ran toward him. He had got his foot caught in a shelf of rock and his mouth was wide open. Kneeling down firmly, Francoise hauled him free. He stood for some time in the sunlight, his face drawn, stupefied by his glimpse of death.

The next day, Madame la Hourie came to thank Francoise. Luc's mother approached her with the same look on her face as she had now: the look of an animal which has just given birth, at once suspicious and beseeching, appealing and defensive.

The corsair of the big portrait had weighed very heavily in the scales of Françoise's marriage to Luc. At the outset, indeed, the very idea of Luc as a husband struck her as absurd. He was so childish, so ignorant, so unstable! A husband ought to take the lead, and she despised anyone who shirked his duty. The rector of Grainfollet was sent to her as an envoy. Aunt Angélique came across the river, exclaiming, "Why, what a chance for you!" Françoise replied, "But I don't love him." The two of them retorted that love was born of marriage, at least, love worthy of the name, the only kind of love that was in question. Then they talked about the Christian home and children, about Providence, about France, about the mistakes due to romanticism, about Luc's religious upbringing. Despite the deep echo which their words awakened in her, they left Françoise only half-convinced.

It was La Hourie who did most in overcoming her repugnance. She was hard put to it to defend herself against the glory and prestige of a great name which she could make her own. It is at once the privilege and the weakness of well-born girls to be so responsive to the past. Sometimes she left Luc's room with her nerves on edge when he inflicted on her, one after the other, his chalices, his ciboriums, all the toys he had kept since his devout childhood. But she calmed down when Madame la Hourie showed her a letter of marque or a warrant as Chevalier of Saint Louis, signed by Louis XIV's own hand. Then she used to hear Luc's mother calling her son "La Hourie," in accordance with the custom of old-country families, whereby the eldest son was known by his surname. So that evening when Luc pestered her with his petitions: "You don't want to marry me? Why don't you want to marry me? Tell me that you will!" it was, above all, to his ancestor that she gave way.

When they rose from the table, Madame la Hourie said, "Have you a minute to spare? Will you come upstairs with me?"

It was into Luc's room that she took Françoise, his boyhood

room which she had preserved intact. At the age of twenty, after a visit with friends, he had suddenly become enthusiastic over the sheerest modern style. Madame la Hourie, who loathed it anywhere else, at once had a partition pulled down and paneling removed in order to obtain bare walls, which were then given a worm-shaped texture with "silexine." Within these walls a Paris decorator installed arm-chairs upholstered with white Morocco leather, low seats in chromium-plated bronze, and a divan-bed fitted with gadgets, doors concealing the telephone, the radio and an electrically heated tray to keep the breakfast hot. After taking an enthusiastic interest in the furnishing, Luc finally refused to sleep in the room, because it was, in fact, quite contrary to his tastes, which tended toward cushions and crowding. With his quiet hypocrisy, he pretended to like it only when he boasted about it to his friends or showed it off to them.

Nevertheless, it was there that, just before his marriage, he came to store all the things of the past which he could not take with him into his new life. The strength concentrated in that heavy furniture, the mystery of those invisible doors, those sliding panels, seemed to him, though he was not even conscious of the fact, a kind of protection, a defense against this unknown girl who attracted him, but at the same time frightened him by the sudden ascendancy she had acquired over him.

Madame la Hourie sat down just on the edge of one of the deep arm-chairs. She loathed the lolling-back for which they were meant. Françoise seated herself on a low stool. She waited for conversation to be resumed, as usual, somewhere in Luc's past, about his first communion or his scarlet fever, his bicycle accident or his tutor's arrival; for her mother-in-law hopped about from one end of his short life to the other. She had even stopped using tricks to impose upon Françoise her harking back to these oft-told tales. She took it for granted that it was the duty of the dead man's wife to listen to them, in fact, that she could not help wanting to hear them. Madame la Hourie started her stories with brief formulas: "I was just thinking," or, quite simply: "I remember." Françoise listened with polite attention; but by now she dared to admit to herself that these trivialities bored her, or indeed, what was worse, that they exasperated her.

But tonight her mother-in-law seemed to hesitate. She even blushed before she said, "I have a confession to make to you, Françoise."

She clenched her hands over and over again, as though she were kneading something, and her head sank lower before she went on, "I have to beg your pardon for something. I've been wanting to do it for weeks, but I couldn't summon up enough courage. It was only this morning, at Mass, that I realized I'd robbed you. . . ."

She sat up straight, hastily took a folded sheet of paper from her bodice, and handed it to Françoise.

"It's a letter he wrote to you from Fécamp, just before he sailed. I read it and I've kept it."

Françoise took the letter with distrustful surprise. She held it for a moment or two without unfolding it. Was the secret of that soul, which she had believed to be empty, about to be suddenly revealed to her? If so, it would mean the end of the precarious calm which she had managed to create.

As she unfolded the letter, Madame la Hourie made her apologies with feverish volubility.

"I swear to you, I opened it quite by mistake. He hadn't put your Christian name on it. As soon as I found that it was for you, I looked for a letter to myself in the envelope. But there wasn't one. You'll read that for yourself. He asks you to make his excuses. He tells you that he hadn't time to write to me. Hadn't time! That's what made me angry. I was frightfully jealous, and still more after his death. His last words were to you. It's made me suffer so much that you must forgive me."

Françoise was not listening to her. She was reading Luc's letter line by line. He had seldom written, perhaps through fear of his spelling, which went astray here and there. It was this that struck her first, these mistakes of his. They brought him back to her, boldly ignorant, boastful of mediocrity, convinced that learning lowered "gentlepeople" and brought them down to the level of schoolmasters, who sold it.

"We're sailing this evening," Luc wrote. "I've seen my cabin. The bed is better than I should have expected. I have a little bathroom, but the water is yellowish. The captain has been very respectful. I could feel that he was flattered to have me as a passenger . . ."

Françoise hastened through the fussy emptiness of trivialities: ten embarrassed lines to make his excuses for not writing to his mother; little instructions about the dogs, the parrots, the care of his launch. Finally, at the foot of the last page, there was this recollection: "I am taking away with me our happy memories of Antibes. I shall see them again in the cold mists where we are going. I shall repeat to myself what you said to me, what I said to you. Do you remember that night of ours at Golfe Juan?"

Suddenly, startled by his boldness, he added a parenthetical sentence: "You mustn't show this letter to Mamma."

When Françoise raised her head after reading the last line, she found her mother-in-law staring at her, with that combative look of hers.

"Well, have you read it?" she demanded. "You mustn't show me that letter! Why not?"

Françoise shrugged her shoulders wearily.

"I've no idea," she replied.

It had just dawned upon her that, if her mother-in-law had given her Luc's letter today, it was from no qualm of conscience, but so that she could cry out at her that "Why not?" which had been consuming her for the past year.

"Yes, why not?" Luc's mother repeated. "Why did he want to hide it from me? Was it because I wasn't capable of understanding that you were his wife, that you had memories between you . . . ? Memories . . . ?"

She sought for a word which she could not find, or from which she shrank.

That, in turn, threw Françoise back into the past. She remembered those hateful days of her honeymoon, which this woman had poisoned with her orders, with her prohibitions, with the fear that she inspired in her son and that seemed to be increased by distance. Françoise saw her again, clinging with her stumpy fingers to the door of the car in which they were about to drive away. She heard her saying, "Your tablets are in the toilet-case. . . . Don't wear your gray suit until the end of the month, it's too light. . . . Don't eat shell-fish; you know they don't agree with you. . . . When you go out in the evening, don't forget to put on your scarf. . . ." She had condescended to use the plural only to command, "Above all, write to me every day! One day without a letter, and I shall go mad!"

In the car, all the way to the station, Luc, sniffing tearfully, sang his mother's praises. Only the train rescued Françoise from this eulogy, because her husband at once lost his head over the little problems of departure: finding their reserved seats, counting the pieces of baggage, choosing between the

34

two services of dinner. At the stations, he got up, went to look out of the door, and announced, "This is Vitré," or "This is Laval," or "This is Le Mans." Then he consulted the time-table, and was annoyed to find every time that the train was four minutes late. "We'll never make that up," he wailed, shaking his head as though over some serious loss. He also said, with an embarrassed little laugh, "We must get used to calling each other '*tu*.' Mamma insists upon it." For Madame la Hourie, as a lady but not a noblewoman, since the corsair had refused a title, would not admit "*vous*" between husband and wife. . . .

"Did he promise to write to you as soon as he arrived at Fécamp?" Madame la Hourie persisted.

"No," replied Françoise.

"Then was he angry with me about something or other? Did he say anything to you?"

"No, of course not."

"Then why didn't he want me to see that letter?"

Madame la Hourie persisted in butting her head against this mark of mistrust. Françoise, for her part, remembered other letters, written from Antibes. "We mustn't tell her that we went to the Casino. . . . We mustn't tell her that I bought that clip for you. . . . We mustn't tell her . . ." They must avoid telling her anything which might suggest that they were in love. Not much difficulty about that!

Now, at the sight of her mother-in-law's face distorted by dreadful jealousy over a dead man, Françoise felt like crying, "You needn't worry. There wasn't anything like that. Never! You were always there, worse than you are now. That night at Golfe Juan! Oh, if only I could tell you about it, call you to account for it!"

It was the memory of that night about which Luc plumed himself, while Françoise could never think about it without disgust, which suddenly made her hold out the letter.

"Keep it," she said.

Madame la Hourie started.

"What?" she replied. "But it's yours. It's not mine."

Françoise laid the letter on a glass table-top.

"You've kept it so long," she retorted.

Her mother-in-law eyed her with intense hope, ill-disguised as reproach. She trembled. A fresh flow of strength made her sit up straight. She clenched her fists.

"I wonder," she murmured, "just what you mean."

Françoise shrugged her shoulders slightly.

"You know quite well," she replied, in a chilly voice. "I mean that he never loved anyone but you. I mean that I was nothing in his life but a pastime, just like all the other pastimes you provided for him, just like this room, for example, just like the dogs and the birds you bought for him before me."

A wave of anger swept through her at the thought of that empty letter.

"You dare to talk like that!" exclaimed Madame la Hourie. She stood up.

"I thought that the two of us could share our memories of him here," she went on. "Am I to understand that I was mistaken?"

Françoise shook her head.

"I haven't got any memories of my own," she said. "I haven't got any memories in which you aren't mixed up."

Her mother-in-law nervously re-arranged some ornaments on the marble top of a chest of drawers. Then, breathless with indignation, she burst out, "Still, there are some moments in married life which belong only to husband and wife. *He* remembered them."

Françoise stared at her hard. Madame la Hourie felt she was on the brink of a candor so threatening that she turned her eyes away.

"I was forgetting the time," she murmured. "It's this afternoon that we're going to Le Mesnil. It's time for us to be thinking about starting."

She came quite close to Françoise. Françoise could barely restrain a shudder when her mother-in-law put her arm around her shoulders.

"Do you mind if we never speak about all this again?" she asked.

Françoise was used to her sudden changes of humor, but never before had she been so tired of them. Madame la Hourie's arm tightened around her shoulders, and she stiffened lest she should flinch, above all, lest she should suddenly break away.

"Tell me, my child," Madame la Hourie went on, "don't you agree?"

"Yes, of course," replied Françoise.

Ten minutes later, the two of them set out in the car. Françoise drove it. At the entrance to the village, she stopped for gasoline. The village consisted of one street, with a squat church, a school, and a score of houses so closely linked together, so alike in their granite, that they looked like a single wall pierced with doors and windows.

Madame Luc, as the villagers had taken to calling Françoise, got out at the grocery, went in, and asked for thirty litres. Three men were drinking bowls of soup at a little table covered with oilcloth. Two women were making purchases at the counter. All of them stopped talking when they saw Françoise and stared at her as though she were unwelcome. She knew why. . . .

When the *Entreprenant,* one of the trawlers belonging to the La Houries, set off on her last voyage, with Luc on board to undertake a few weeks' fishing by way of his investiture as a shipowner, she carried a crew hand-picked by Madame la Hourie in person. In order that, during his exile, her son should have around him faces he knew, men who were or might become indebted to him, she visited all the fishermen's houses in the village and, with the aid of handsome bonuses and gratuities, recruited the best sailors in the district. When the trawler was lost with all hands, just after she reached the fishing-grounds, her wreck decimated the village. Eleven of its men went down with her.

From that moment Françoise was conscious of the implacable resentment of their womenfolk. "The old one," as they called Madame la Hourie, had taken their men away from them almost by force, their men who should have sailed in other ships, ships that had come back. Then, as soon as she was able to go out and talk to people again, obsessed as she was by her own loss, she had blasphemed the loss of others. The help she brought them was accepted with hatred, because she dared to say, "Of course, it was your men's job. But my son. . . ."

When she had gone and the door was shut behind her, widows or bereaved mothers looked at one another and demanded, "Did you hear what she said?" Some of them cursed her, parted their curtains to follow her along the street with venomous glances, pressed their mouths to the windows to hurl enraged imprecations after her.

Never, it was true, had compensation for the loss of a crew been paid so promptly, so liberally. Madame la Hourie doubled the insurance benefits. When she announced this in the homes of the eleven lost men, she said, "It's in memory of my son, so that you'll remember him."

But the hostile village translated this, "It's because she's afraid."

Françoise knew all this. As she picked up her change from the brass tray, she could still feel the antipathy in which she shared, she, the stranger, who had been left rich after the disaster. Before she left, she inquired about the shopkeeper's daughter, who had been ill with measles.

"She's over it," replied the woman. "She went back to school yesterday."

"I thought it was forbidden to send children back for a fortnight," said Françoise.

"Well, what should I do with her here for a fortnight? She was driving me wild," said the woman. "I haven't got money to pay servants to look after her."

Françoise realized that she had touched her on the raw. As soon as she was outside, everyone would say, "Did you hear that? What business is it of hers?"

"Maybe," she retorted, "but she's still contagious and it's the other children that catch her measles who'll have to pay."

She waited for a moment on the threshold for a reply, but none came and she went out.

She drove fast. Sitting beside her, Madame la Hourie stared steadily at the rubber mat beneath her feet, not saying a word. She hated this cabriolet, because it belonged to Françoise. One day she had babbled advice to be careful, but Françoise had stopped the car at the sidewalk, and declared, "I can't drive if you talk to me." Since then, Madame la Hourie had kept quiet; but she put up with the cabriolet only in case of necessity, when the Delage, which Grioul drove, was out of action, as it was at the moment.

At Châteauneuf, Françoise swung around eastward toward Dol. She passed through a village with thatched cottages. The thick thatch had been carefully clipped back and hung above the windows like a cap's peak over the eyes. The weather was hazy and distance was blurred. Françoise slowed down and looked around.

She found herself in the heart of a strange region, on the verge of Saint-Coulban Pond. She remembered her father talking about it as a region to be feared, where the Chouans had once allied themselves with the bogs and the marches. From the road, she could see to her right long strips of pale water stagnating between tongues of low-lying land, bristling with dry rushes and broken by clumps of shrubs, still black. Flat meadows, green-bronze, like all water-logged land, ended in sheets of gleaming bog. Rows of stunted, twisted pollard-oaks meandered here and there on the banks of the dead water. It was said that naphtha had been found under the soggy, cease-lessly shuddering soil, and that a village, evangelized by Saint Colomban, had been swallowed up for its sins and lay beneath the mournful surface of the pond. Fossilized trees, beech and walnut, rose from the depths here and there, and their notched branches writhed over the water in fantastic, inky designs. In hot summers, the marshy ground sometimes caught fire spon-taneously, and set the rain storms boiling. Once the fires were out, there were left quicksands of red-hot ashes, in which men and beasts were swallowed up. Every evening flocks of crows, driven from the woods of Ponthual by the traffic on the Dinard road, circled over Saint-Coulban Pond and perched on its willows for the night.

Paying too much attention to the passing of the somber

landscape, Françoise slowed down so much that she had to change gear to climb a short, but steep hill. At the top of it, to her left, an avenue of elms opened in between white pillars. She turned into it. At the end rose a gray manor-house, flanked by a pepper-pot turret, with a short flight of steps overgrown with woody hydrangea. Françoise stopped the car at the foot of the steps.

A housemaid, whose rosy cheeks and startled eyes suggested that she had not long left her farm, ushered the guests into a spacious drawing room. She closed a French window facing a neglected field on which cows were grazing. The sheen from the meadows filled the room with the green light of an aquarium. A wood fire danced in the hearth. The furniture was of yellow wood, upholstered with worn rep.

Two women came in, one helping the other: Madame de Guersac and her companion. Comtesse de Guersac walked with very short, stiff, careful steps. For years she had been crippled by chronic rheumatism. The hand she held out to her visitors was deformed. It was hard to tell her age, especially when she was walking, for her fear of a false step, always punished by a shoot of pain, petrified her features. Her companion was a tall, handsome brunette with bold eyes. Her strong body scarcely seemed to feel the Comtesse's weight, and her mouth, vividly outlined with lipstick, looked like a challenge in that faded setting. She led the Comtesse to an arm-chair, and stood upright with a toss of her head, because Madame la Hourie did not appear to have noticed her. Only Françoise had shaken hands with her. It was said that she was the Comte's mistress, and that he had made his wife take her as her companion.

Madame de Guersac apologized for her husband's absence.

"He'll be so sorry to have missed you. But now that the trout season has started, he spends all his days fishing."

41

"And he never catches anything," said her companion, with a fleeting smile.

"You're exaggerating, Anna," the Countess corrected her, timidly. "He caught two fish last week."

"But he confessed to me that they were a present from the keeper," retorted Anna.

Madame de Guersac turned in annoyance toward Madame la Hourie.

"I'm so glad to see you," she said. "I think about you so much, especially at night. Thinking about other people's troubles is a rather selfish way of forgetting about yourself and your own." Her visitors inquired about her health, but she replied that she had no desire to talk about it. She was only too happy to forget it for a few minutes in their company.

She tried to lean toward her friend, but a stab of her rheumatism thrust her back, and she reverted to the position in which she felt the least pain, her arms away from her body, her hands, resting palms down, on the arms of her chair, her fingers spread out.

"But what about you?" she asked. "What a martyrdom for you, my poor Lucie! And I can't even go to see you!"

Madame la Hourie shook her head.

"God wouldn't take me," she said. "But it wasn't for want of asking him!"

They fell silent. Then Anna got up and went out. She had to give orders about the tea. Freed from her presence, Madame la Hourie instantly leaned forward and started talking. She retold the story she told everywhere. She began with the telegram which she had read and reread in the hall, in a daze: "Have every reason fear trawler *Entreprenant* lost with all hands." Then she described her departure for Paris, her siege of shipping companies and government offices to find out what they knew and enjoin them to make further inquiries. Finally, she recalled her return to Plangomeur in despair, her vigils at the drawing-room window—the one from which you could see right down the drive. For she had tirelessly awaited the arrival of a miraculous message which would deny the dreadful news. It was there that her daughter-in-law had found her one evening, in a faint on the floor.

"When I came to, I was so sure that I was going to die. Oh, if only wanting to die were enough! And my nerves were in such a state. I had to stay in the dark. I couldn't stand any light."

Françoise had been listening with resignation to this tale she had heard over and over again. Suddenly she stirred. The echo of a harsh voice reached her ears: "We let in some light." She was astonished that this memory should come to her so clearly, and that a word should suffice to recall it. Once more she saw the man's bold face bending over her, his long, strong hands on the edge of the door, the sparkle in his dark eyes. Then she said to herself, "He's only a foreman," and dismissed him from her mind.

But it was only to be all the more intensely irritated by the eulogy of Luc in which her mother-in-law was now indulging. It was the ritual peroration of her story. Once Françoise had listened to it with the deference due to funeral prayers. But now she knew only too well that the drowned man had been nothing but a weak, worthless creature. His cowardice, his hypocrisy, his wheedling, his insensitivity, had first distressed her, and then aroused her anger. This creature she had found once more in every line of his letter which her mother-in-law had stolen. So, as she listened to the two old women alternately singing his praises, her nerves were set on edge. She rebelled against her mute role of guardian of his tomb. She was less ready than ever to submit to it.

"All you have suffered," Madame de Guersac wound up, "will be credited to him. To suffer through the dead means helping them."

But Madame la Hourie slowly shook her head with a besotted smile of ecstasy.

"Poor boy!" she replied. "He doesn't need any prayers. God welcomed him at once."

At this moment, Anna came back, pushing a tea-wagon in front of her. She did not seem to notice that the conversation stopped dead at her entrance. She started serving tea. Madame la Hourie persisted in refusing to look at her. Françoise, on the other hand, was surprised that she did not feel shocked by the assurance of this servant-mistress, by her air of authority. A sweater of aggressive garnet-red violently accentuated her ochre make-up. Its collar curled back from a neck that was too short, but round and smooth. Françoise noticed, too, the silk stockings on her legs, more trim and slender than her strong body would lead one to expect. Anna radiated sensuous health, satisfaction with her physique. Françoise appreciated it, despite herself, with a rather shamefaced sense of conspiracy. With this fine girl, life itself came back into the faded drawing-room.

Madame de Guersac talked about the weather. The spring was early. The tulip-tree in the park had just opened its buds.

Anna, who was pouring out tea, turned toward Françoise.

"Do you know it?" she asked.

"No," replied Françoise.

"You can't see it from here. Come and have a look at it."

Madame de Guersac endorsed her suggestion.

44

"Yes, this is just the time to admire it," she agreed. "It lasts such a short time. The slightest frost, and it's blighted."

Anna led Françoise to the last window at the end of the drawing room, from which one could see all the west part of the park. In the middle of a meadow, springing from a clump of bushes, the tulip-tree displayed its huge bouquet of rose. Its budding flowers, as large as water lilies, shone resplendent on the dark branches. Françoise exclaimed in admiration, but Anna shrugged her shoulders.

"It's almost too lovely compared with the rest," she said. "The park is all neglected. Monsieur Henry doesn't care about anything but the rabbits that browse in it. I said to him, 'You ought to cut down that tulip-tree. In this unkempt park of yours, it looks as shocking as a jewel on a dirty woman.' He didn't say 'No.' "

She laughed that sudden, overdone laugh of hers.

"Oh, that would be a sin!" Françoise protested.

Anna replied only by a shrug of her shoulders which seemed to be her habitual gesture. Then she asked, "Do you see the bushes round the tree? What do you think they are?"

"They look like mallows," replied Françoise.

"They're not, exactly. They're ketmias, and their flowers change color. They're pretty rare, it seems. Monsieur Henry's father brought them from the Indies. The flowers are white in the morning, they turn rosy in the afternoon, and then, toward nightfall, they become crimson, deeper than this sweater."

Suddenly she lowered her voice.

"I remember your husband went crazy about them the last time he was here, when he saw them in flower. He insisted on having some cuttings, but I don't think they struck root at your place."

"I've never seen anything like them at Plangomeur. When do they flower?"

"From June to October. Monsieur la Hourie came here in July, and they were in full flower. Yes, I'm sure it was in July. He was just back from Auvergne."

"From Auvergne?"

The name surprised Françoise. Luc was usually so prolix about the smallest journey he made. He had not spared her an account of a pilgrimage to Lourdes, or a holiday at the seaside. But he had never mentioned Auvergne.

Anna seemed still more astonished at her surprise. She stared at Françoise with distrustful attention.

"Yes, from Auvergne," she repeated. "He stayed several months there. . . ."

Then it dawned on her that Luc's widow really did not know anything about it. She looked away.

"After all," she said, "he may not have mentioned it to you."

There was a hint of irony in the affected indifference of her tone which Françoise did not fail to notice. She turned around and tried to look into Anna's eyes.

A penetrating, raucous noise interrupted her. It was like a siren in a fog, or the bellow of an enormous bull, one of those fighting bellows that stretch its neck and its whole body. But, instead of dying away, it ended in a hiccup, as though someone had strangled the cry in the monstrous throat.

Anna drew herself up. Head thrown back, eyes shining, she exclaimed, "The Bellow!"

Seated in her arm-chair, Madame de Guersac listened with an air of alarm, as one listens to the approach of a distant danger. Cut short, Madame la Hourie pursed her lips and waited till she could continue her conversation.

Anna, all excitement, took three strides which brought her into the middle of the drawing room, Françoise at her heels.

"I've missed it again," she cried. "Yesterday you could hear it from Saint-Jouan, but I was too far away to go and have a look. Today it's nearer, but it's not so loud. It's 'stifled,' as the good people say."

"But what is it?" asked Françoise.

"Haven't you heard about the Saint-Coulban Bellow?" replied Anna. "Why, it's one of our local curiosities! It's come back to us this year after more than twenty years of silence, so it seems. According to your taste, it's the scream of an accursed priest swallowed up in the pond, or the cry of a starred heron. More likely it's an escape of compressed air from the bog."

"They say," murmured Madame de Guersac, "that it brings bad luck and foretells black years."

Anna laughed, longer than usual.

"Everyone in this part of the world is a bit mad," she declared. "They said that the Bellow was dead, and now that they've heard it again, they can't sleep at night any more. Monsieur Henry swore that he'd go and look for it, and that he'd find it. It was arranged that we were to go together. If he's found it all by himself, I'll never forgive him."

Madame de Guersac shook her head slowly.

"He won't find it," she said.

Anna turned toward her.

"I'll bet you believe in the Bellow, don't you, Madame?"

For once, Madame la Hourie acknowledged Anna's existence.

"Since you can hear it," she said drily, "you can't help believing in it."

47

But Anna brushed the argument aside with a swift sweep of her long hand.

"I'm talking about the real Bellow, the supernatural Bellow," she insisted. "It isn't a heron, or a bittern, or the whistling of air in the bog. It's something else, something mysterious, something that can't be found. That's what you believe in, isn't it, Madame?"

Madame de Guersac shrugged her shoulders.

"I don't know whether I believe in it," she replied, "but I confess that I have some respect for certain fears, and I don't like them to be mocked."

Struck by her words, Françoise looked at her. She was staring at something far away, and her mournful look was sadder than ever. But Anna shrugged her shoulders once more.

"Mocked?" she retorted. "Why should they be, when all you have to do is face them, and you find them empty?"

Madame de Guersac shook her head again.

"Not always," she said.

THE electrical engineers arrived one morning in April, as though for an attack.

It was eight o'clock, and there was a white frost. They waited in their black leather jackets at the entrance gate. Behind them, like an ancient catapult, rose the steel crane of the crab-truck, and, behind that again, stretched the convoy of sling-wagons to which the concrete posts were tied.

One of them rang the bell. He was bareheaded, and wore a fur jacket, plus fours, and shoes with thick soles.

Grioul made his appearance, put his big, round head next to the bars, and looked suspiciously at the gang with his small, piercing eyes.

"We've come to start work on the line," said the man who had rung the bell.

Grioul did not open the gate. He leaned sideways to get a better look at the column of heavy trucks at the end of the drive.

"Do you want to bring all those in?" he demanded, in a hostile tone.

"Yes, and the sooner the better."

"I must go and tell Madame."

Grioul turned his back on them, and took himself off with his rolling gait, dragging his clogs along the gravel.

"And stir your stumps a bit!" shouted the man in the fur jacket, irritated by his slowness.

The rest of the gang jeered.

"A snail could give him a handicap," said one of them.

From the threshold of Madame la Hourie's room, Grioul informed her, "The engineers are here." He added, "And all they've brought with them!"

Madame la Hourie was reading. She closed her book.

"I don't want to have anything to do with them," she said.

"Shall I let them in?" asked Grioul.

Madame la Hourie shuddered. She stiffened in her chair.

"It's terrible!" she exclaimed. "Nowadays anyone can force his way into your property and knock down and smash up whatever he likes. They'll destroy everything. And all the owner can do is put up with it!"

She reopened her book and pretended to go on with her reading, but red patches stained her pale cheeks, and her lower lip quivered.

"They're waiting at the gate," Grioul persisted.

"All right, let them in!"

Grioul was turning away when a cry from Madame la Hourie called him back.

"Wait! There's one thing, understand, that I'll never let them touch, not on any account, and that's Monsieur's summer-house."

"It might be better for Madame to speak to them herself," suggested Grioul.

Madame la Hourie shook her head.

"I've told you already that I won't see them. Go and open the gate for them, and ask Madame Luc to come and speak to me."

When the gate was open, the trucks and wagons invaded the garden. The man who seemed to be in charge stationed himself at the end of the main flower-bed and watched the turns. Once, when the end of a post threatened to cut the heads off

50

some flowers, he signaled to the truck concerned to stop, and jumped up to the steering-wheel, pushing the driver farther along the seat.

"You're cutting it too fine," he said. "Let me do it."

Leaning out, he corrected the angle without backing, and made the turn without even grazing a tulip. Grioul, who was watching the invasion morosely, cast a black glance at him for robbing him of such a fine chance of cursing indignantly. But when the last post, wabbling between its chains, had been brought into the park, Grioul found that the heavy wheels had sunk into the paths around his beds even more deeply than he had feared. Then indeed he could swear, fling down the spade which he had been nursing, and declare that it was no use tiring himself out any more.

"I want you to do something for me, Françoise," said Madame la Hourie. "Would you keep an eye on what those men are doing and tell them that I won't let them touch La Hourie's summer-house?"

When she said "La Hourie" instead of "Luc," it meant that the prestige of the family was involved.

"Very well, Mamma," replied Françoise. "I'll go and see about it."

In her bedroom, she had heard the trucks entering the grounds and had automatically gone to the window. But she drew back immediately, because she recognized the man in the fur jacket guiding the convoy as the man who had held her up on the road. Her recoil was so involuntary that she had to stop and think about it. An unexpected meeting with a passer-by should not make such an impression on her as all that. This man had interested her, perhaps more than she had imagined. Really, she was getting ridiculous.

Françoise made her way to the end of the park down a long avenue of gray beech trees, already covered by a mist of fresh verdure. Mossy banks rose on either side, and, through the still-leafless branches, the sun poured down upon the moss, making it greener than ever, and upon young fir trees, setting their needles gleaming. Soon the spur of rock which the estate thrust into the heart of marsh and slime narrowed down. It turned into a kind of bare jetty, sprinkled with holly bushes, which overlooked the dreary stretch of low-lying land from a height of about a hundred feet. From some distance away Françoise could see the tangle of wheels and limbers amid which the men were busy. They were freeing the concrete posts from their encircling chains and lining them up on the ground.

It was his voice that Françoise recognized first, his impatient, rather hoarse voice, giving orders behind the crane.

"Clear away there, for Heaven's sake! What's all this mess?"

When he saw Françoise coming along the path, his eyebrows went up. His men, too, surprised to see her, stood erect and stared at her. He let her make her way toward him amid the trucks. Then he saluted curtly, and asked, "So you've come to see the enemy on the spot, have you?"

"My mother-in-law, Madame la Hourie, is afraid of her park being too badly damaged," replied Françoise, in a level tone which marked the distance between them. "She's sent me to ask you what you intend to cut down."

He turned around and surveyed the scene of his work. He seemed perplexed.

"It's rather difficult to tell you as early as this," he said. "The ground is so rocky that we may have to change our plans. This morning I'm going to mark half a dozen trees which will be in our way. For the rest, we'll do as little damage as we can. I promised you that before, for that matter."

He glanced at Françoise quickly, and, when she nodded, by way of admitting that she remembered their meeting, he introduced himself.

"I'm André Maurière, regional engineer of the Western Electric Company."

Françoise could feel that he expected her to show some surprise. She simply nodded again, curtly. Then, with all the persistence of a sportsman astride his hobby-horse, he explained what she had not asked him.

"I've made a point of keeping an eye on everything myself, because this is one of the hardest places. Running a line over here is like doing a cross-word puzzle. One couldn't imagine a better excuse for shaking the dust of the office off one's feet. I always get on an outside job whenever I can."

Françoise said nothing, long enough for the conversation he had started to lapse without offense. Then she pointed to a queer building, standing on a little grassy mound a few paces away to the left. It was a hexagonal pavilion, made of logs nailed together slantwise, with little windows and a bulbous zinc roof with rounded angles like that of a Chinese kiosk.

"Above all," she said, "you mustn't touch that summer-house. My mother-in-law . . ." She paused, almost imperceptibly, and went on, ". . . and I are very fond of it."

Maurière stared at the absurd structure, and had difficulty in repressing a smile.

"It was my husband who had it built," Françoise added, more curtly than ever. "He died a year ago."

Maurière indicated that he knew.

"The summer-house won't be in our way for running the

53

line," he said. "But all that will probably be a bit trampled down."

He pointed to the flowering periwinkles that carpeted the knoll and its surroundings.

"I'll try to save some of them."

"Thank you," said Françoise. "And what about the transformer? Where are you going to put that?"

"I'm not sure yet, but I promise you I'll do what I can to hide it."

"At best, it will look hideous."

At Françoise's words, the engineer's face hardened, and he turned sharply toward the summer-house. He was on the point of retorting with a sarcastic remark. After all, the white cube of a transformer would mar the view less than the elaborate imbecility of the lodge which he was asked to preserve. But he contented himself with shrugging his shoulders.

"Don't you think that usefulness sometimes excuses ugliness?" he asked.

Françoise reflected, suddenly interested in the question.

"I really don't know," she confessed.

Maurière put his hands back into his pockets, and moved his left foot forward to take up a firmer stance.

"Well, I think it does," he said, "and I think so because I've seen it. When we work in some parts of Lower Brittany, and we have to demolish a pig-sty to make way for the line, the people would welcome us with pitchforks, if they dared. The boys lie in wait and throw stones at us. It's still worse when we have to tackle the fronts of farm buildings to drive in our stanchions. The stones are only stuck together with sand, and sometimes a whole stretch of wall falls down. All the family stand gaping, as though we were a band of brigands making an attack."

54

He started walking back and forth. Occasionally he stopped suddenly and stared at Françoise, by way of making his point with his eyes as well as his voice.

When he did so, Françoise noticed the tautness of his clean-shaven face, with the bones showing strongly under the tight-drawn skin. He talked with his head flung back, like a runner making a sprint. When he laughed at a memory, his sudden laugh reminded Françoise of Anna's laugh as she listened to the Bellow in the drawing room at Le Mesnil. He had the same assured laugh, revealing white, strong teeth, the laugh of a hungry man at the sight of a meal.

"There's one moment I wouldn't miss for anything," he went on, "and that's the moment when I switch on the current, and the whole house lights up. You should just see their faces, their open mouths, when they look at the electric lamps. Their bins and their benches and their cupboards shine so that they hardly recognize them. Some of them clasp their hands. Others laugh and say, 'Just imagine that!' Don't you think that ought to make us popular?"

"Perhaps," replied Françoise.

"Very well, then!"

Maurière turned round in front of her and laughed again. Then he asked, "I suppose you light the chateau with a battery and a motor? I must have a look and see what use you might make of the line. If we ran a lead from it for you, you'd have better and more even light."

"We'd have the breakdowns, too!"

"Quite so. Forcing people to return for a few minutes to their candles and their oil-lamps is the only way we've yet found of making ourselves appreciated."

They had reached the edge of the spur. In front of them, down below, stretched bright green meadows, riddled with water-holes. Maurière lowered his voice as he said, "I'm glad you came."

His tone was equivocal, exploratory. It made Françoise draw in at once.

"My mother-in-law would have come herself," she replied, "but she doesn't go out in the morning. In any case, she counts on you to see that the least possible damage is done."

Maurière turned back toward the medley of vehicles. His face wore the hard, impenetrable mask with which he met any resistance, any refusal.

"You may tell your mother-in-law that the barbarians and their leader will try not to make themselves too odious. But, as people say, what must be, must be. . . . Excuse me, they've gone to sleep over there."

He pointed to the men standing idle between the high wheels. Then he bowed, very slightly, and strode rapidly toward them.

To get back to the house, Françoise did not follow the main path, because she would have to pass the men and their vehicles. A path led to the right, between fir and holly. Françoise started along it, in order to make herself invisible to the engineers at once.

When she reached the bed where Grioul was thinning out a border, she stopped.

"They haven't done too much damage?" she asked.

The gardener shrugged his shoulders, and pointed to the rutted paths.

"Unless they'd driven over my flowers, they could scarcely have done worse," he replied. "I'll certainly wait till they're gone before putting all this right. You might as well spit in the air as take a rake to it now."

From there, Françoise went straight to Madame la Hourie's room.

A girl with a spotty face, wearing a white apron, one of the two housemaids who were dusting the armor in the long corridor on the first floor, turned away from polishing a boarding cutlass and told her, "Madame will have to go back."

Françoise was going to ask why, but the girl, only recently arrived from an orphanage and still rather stupid, started polishing again furiously, shaking her shoulders by way of stressing her conscientiousness. Françoise went into her mother-in-law's room. Madam la Hourie had a work-basket beside her, and was rolling wool into a ball nervously, with extremely quick movements of her stumpy fingers. When her daughter-in-law came in, she broke the thread.

"I've just come back from the park," said Françoise. "They won't touch the summer-house, and they'll do as little damage as they can."

Madame la Hourie shook her head. Then she raised her arms and suddenly dropped them again, as though she were throwing something away. Finally, she too said, "You'll have to go back."

Françoise was used to this kind of repeated incoherence at Plangomeur. Madame la Hourie always cleared it up with a flood of words.

"I thought about it the moment you'd gone out," she said. "They won't touch the summer-house without telling us. But what about the fir tree? Yes, what about the fir tree? You know, the one I showed you."

Endlessly, she went over the story of the Christmas trees again. Luc could not bear to see them wither and weep when they were burned. So his mother had the trees taken up with their roots. They were put in tubs and replanted in the park after Candlemas. The one Madame la Hourie was talking about was one of the few that had struck root again and grown. It

had been replanted among the beeches on the spur. Yes, Françoise must go at once and tell the men that she forbade them
not only to fell it, but even to lop the smallest bit off it. Perhaps
Grioul might even put a fence around it.

"There's an engineer in charge of the work," replied Fran-
çoise, in her level voice. "It was he whom I saw this morning.
It isn't for us to disturb ourselves by bringing him instructions.
It's for him to come and get them."

Madame la Hourie tried to hide a blush at this reprimand.
With an embarrassed, wheezing little laugh, she said, very
quickly, "Of course, if there's an engineer, that's quite different. I didn't know there was one. Otherwise, I wouldn't have
asked you to go there yourself. I'll go at once and send for
him to come here."

Twenty minutes later, Grioul came back from the park.

"The engineer has just gone," he reported. "It seems he
won't be back for four or five days. But I've seen the trees he
marked before he went, and Monsieur's fir tree is one of them."

"Go back at once, my child!" exclaimed Madame la Hourie.

Françoise went back. The workmen took no notice of her.
Were they to be pestered like this all day? First this girl, then
the boss, and now here she was back again! They had had to
move three posts already to avoid trampling on the violets.

Françoise was at once conscious of their hostility. She went
and stood in front of Luc's fir tree—a spindly tree, barely as
thick as an arm. It was notched with a determined cut of an
ax, which laid bare the rosy wood inside the bark. In such a
tone that all the men stopped working and stared at her, she
said, "I absolutely forbid you to cut down this tree."

Four days later, Maurière came into the drawing room. He
was barely inside before he tackled her.

"So it seems you forbade my men to cut down the fir tree?"

He stood at the window, his hands behind his back, just as he stood when he was at work.

"They told me you'd forbidden them to cut it down," he went on. "As that would change the whole layout of the posts, they've been waiting for me to settle the question. I was at the other end of Brittany. So, though they have all their gear here, they've done nothing but twiddle their thumbs. I don't like that."

"And still less do we like your trying to cut down trees of which we're fond!" retorted Françoise.

Maurière took a couple of steps toward the middle of the room. Then he turned around.

"That fir tree!" he exclaimed. "If it were even a fine tree! But it's such a wretched thing. I don't know what it's doing there. Another keepsake, is it?"

He asked the question with such sudden insolence that Françoise was on the point of showing him the door. But she merely nodded and said, "Precisely."

Maurière made a sweeping movement with his right hand.

"I'm sorry, Madame," he said, "but I can't go on taking into account everything that may present itself. Yesterday it was a summer-house and the flowers growing round it. So far, so good. But today it's a tree that recalls something or other. Tomorrow it may be a rock on which you used to sit with someone. . . ."

"Are you aware that you're being odious?" demanded Françoise.

Maurière was walking up and down. He stopped, struck by her words.

"Maybe I am," he replied. "Indeed, I'm sure I am, since you say so. After all, it's none of my business to know why you're fond of that fir tree, or even to try and find out. I'm just a man who plants posts. But I must plant them in a straight line. So I can only tell you one thing. I can't help felling that fir tree. I'm sorry."

He made his way toward the door, his brow furrowed. As he passed her, Françoise said, slowly, "So you're going to fell it?"

"Yes, this evening."

That afternoon, with Madame la Hourie, Françoise listened to the crackle of falling trees. She agreed with the old lady's verbose indignation, by way of stifling the vague sense of connivance in the sacrilege which she felt deep down in herself. In the evening, when the last truck had gone, she went down to the spur in the park. The fir tree lay, hacked, flush with the ground. Françoise stared at it for a long time.

When she came back and announced that she had failed, that the tree had been felled, Madame la Hourie stood up and started trembling—a queer tremble straight up and down, with stops and starts, that looked like the beginning of a dance.

"They've dared to do that!" she exclaimed.

She sat down again. She kept on shaking her head. Little by little she assessed the scale of the outrage. Then she stared at her daughter-in-law with acute distrust, with an insight which increased second by second.

"I made a mistake," she said. "I should have gone and talked to them *myself*."

IN HER father's time at Le Fraô, toward evening, Françoise had often heard the sound of a horn. It set the farmers and farm-hands about the place sniggering. Her father frowned and plunged his hands in his pockets. In her kitchen, Maclovie shook her head and made a face of contempt. One day Françoise asked her, "Who's blowing that horn, and why?" The old woman mumbled through her teeth, "It's nothing. Just something nasty."

It was not until later that she learned, by accident, that a neighboring squire, hirsute and half-crazy, whom no one ever visited now, was the horn-blower. He blew it to summon his mistress, Mathurine, a farm-girl, from the fields or the woods. Abjectly submissive to his summons, the girl promptly flung down her sheaf of corn or her bundle of wood and made her way to his so-called chateau, while jeering peasants chanted "Turine, Turine, Turine!" like a fanfare as she passed.

Nothing on earth seemed so despicable to Françoise as this horn-blowing and the response to it, from the depths of the woods, of this wretched girl, bestial in her drab obedience.

Françoise remembered this one morning when she was tempted to go down to the place where the engineers were working. A motor horn yelped at the gate to demand admission. Doubtless it was Maurière's car. The hoarse summons struck Françoise as being meant for her. But she felt that she, too, would be obeying the horn if she went back to the spur in the park.

Still, it was without impatience that she listened to the blows

61

of picks and drills. The engineers had broken down the wall of silence which had imprisoned her for months. The rumble of their trucks, the vibration of their borers, the bursts of their blasting, had made Madame la Hourie retreat into a room at the back where the din was deadened. By driving her from the rooms dedicated to Luc, which were all at the front, they had suspended the punctilious worship of the dead man, and Françoise decided that she was grateful to them for it.

There remained the man who had felled Luc's fir tree, who had been determined to fell it, and whom her mother-in-law hated. Madame la Hourie had sent for Maurière as soon as he came back, and, in Françoise's presence, reproached him with the outrage. She had spoken clearly, without storming or gesticulating. She had gone out of her way to wound him. "It wasn't even a question of delicacy, Monsieur. It was simply a question of good manners. I regret it all the more on your account."

Maurière listened to her, standing still, his eyes fixed on a flower in the carpet. Then he said, "The best advice I can give you, Madame, is to make a complaint to the Company," and he went out. Françoise learned afterward from Grioul, who had heard it from the engineers, that he had gone back to Lower Brittany to inspect a crack in a dam.

This morning, she had ordered the cabriolet to be ready at ten o'clock. The night before, she had reminded her mother-in-law: "Tomorrow is my day for Rocmarin, Mamma."

On the first Thursday in every month, she paid a visit to her aunt, Mademoiselle de Caradeuc, who lived in a queer house on a granite promontory on the other side of the Rance.

"Don't forget to give dear Angélique a kiss from me," said her mother-in-law, just as she was starting. "And tell her how much I think about her."

Madame la Hourie had known the formidable old maid ever since their schooldays, and she hated and feared her enough to keep a place for her in her thoughts.

At the end of the drive, Françoise found one side of the gate shut. This surprised her, for the gate was always left open in the morning for the engineers. She stopped the car; but, before she had time to get out and reopen it, Maurière appeared from among the trees and hastened to it.

"Just a moment!" he said, as he opened it.

Françoise imagined that he had arranged this obstacle and had been lying in wait for her. The idea displeased her. She was about to drive on when Maurière held up his hand and came to the door of the car.

"One of my trucks tore off a hinge this morning," he explained. "The gate is twisted and shuts of its own accord. I've just come to have a look at the damage. I was on my way back when I heard your car."

He clasped the window-ledge, just as he had done at their first meeting. He bent over, and went on, "We don't see you any more. Does that mean you're going to let us destroy whatever we like, without even showing your teeth at us? What a pity!"

He leaned on the ledge.

"Is it because you're angry with me about that fir tree? But you're not, you know. Your mother-in-law is; but you're not."

Françoise stared at him, taken aback. He shook his head to emphasize his denial, and laughed, the laugh of a handsome fellow. The perfect curve of his lips disturbed her.

"In fact, that's why I didn't say anything," he added. "Anything your mother-in-law might want didn't mean a thing, once you agreed with me."

"But I didn't!" Françoise protested.

"Oh, yes, you did. You don't know how to lie. You're blushing."

He was amused at this as though it were a fleeting confusion. But Françoise, for her part, knew that very few people, very few things, in her life had ever had the power to make her blush. Frequent blushes meant nothing; one cancelled out the other. Françoise had had girl friends whose cheeks it amused her to light up in this way, like lamps, whenever she liked, by teasing them in a way that never failed. But she blushed only when the deep springs of her being were troubled. So she preserved a precise memory of her rare blushes. They had enlightened her about herself, just as they had given her away to other people.

"But there are some things I want to tell you," Maurière went on. "Are you afraid of listening to them? No? Then perhaps you're not interested in them? Maybe. But that's no reason why I shouldn't say them. There must be some place in the house where I can talk to you alone, without the good lady. I'll come tomorrow. So it's *au revoir?*"

He stretched out his hand, wide open. Then, as Françoise kept her own hands resting on the steering-wheel, he suddenly seized one of her wrists, raised it, and pressed his lips against her bare skin, between her glove and her sleeve.

As soon as he had let go, she lost sight of him. He stepped back behind the low hood, and waited for her to drive on. It was a moment or two before she managed to do so.

"I never said a word. I didn't resist him. Yes, of course I had time. He was watching me, while he kissed my wrist, to see whether I should let him. What's happening to me, that I should submit to that? Am I going the same way as Hélène?"

"Come on, hurry up!"

Françoise reached the ferry, after parking her car at the little restaurant, as though in a dream. She went down the bit of steep path leading to the slippery jetty. The ferryman was already casting off, and called to her to hurry. She did so, and the man held out his hand to her to help her on board, for the boat was rising and falling alongside the wall, rubbing against a motor-tire stuffed with straw which served as a buffer.

Françoise put her foot on the side of the boat, rose with the swell, and jumped on board. The ferryman pushed away from the jetty with the end of an oar, and the boat set off across the river. Two women from Plouër were already sitting on the seat. They held big black baskets in their laps, and both of them had folded their hands on top of them, just in the same way. Without making a move, the two of them had a good look at the new passenger.

Often the crossing required much maneuvering. When the tide was flowing the boat had to go upstream, close inshore, and then put out into the current and drift sideways to the other bank.

This time, the slack of the tide enabled the ferryman to row straight across without much effort. Françoise had always been responsive to the sense of peace which the river exhaled. Once again she surrendered herself to it, and with a haste which was the measure of her disturbance. She felt as though she were panting after being pursued; but this feeling was relieved by the coolness of the air, the slow rise and fall of the waves. Even the rhythmical lament of the oars in their thole-pins soothed her.

But she knew that this was only a truce. A question had been raised, and she had to answer it. Her fragile widowhood no longer protected her, either against others, or against herself. It was not by his words that Maurière had taken possession of her. Everything he said was commonplace and coarse, except perhaps when he spoke about his work. She was not going to lie to herself for the first time in her life. What attracted her was his firm mouth, his laugh, his moist teeth, his thick fair hair into which caressing fingers might sink, the supple strength of his athletic body. It was his body that attracted her —just his body. Was it possible?

A sudden jar, as the stem of the boat struck the timbers of the quay, told her that she had reached the other side.

She stepped on to the sloping jetty. An angler, wearing rubber boots, was keeping an eye on his big red cork. Bait swam in his bucket. Spring was already laying its burden on the trees, and the sun-smitten slope before her seemed steeper. She walked for some minutes along the road, and then turned to the left along the cliff path which followed the river. But she could no longer see the river, for the path was sunken, like a trench, between broom and black-currant bushes. The path crossed the point, and then ran downhill again, in steep turns where Françoise had to watch her step for roots and stones. It led her to a wide cove, where it suddenly vanished in the shining clay.

The cove was semi-circular, hemmed in by rocks crowned with woods. The blue river enclosed it to the east, and boats lay stuck in its slime: pleasure yachts, luggers with tarpaulins kept taut by interlacing ropes, black fishing boats, all of them sweating tar. Some stood upright on their keels, others lay on their sides, and their mooring-chains made networks of gray traps across the mud. Most striking of all, dominating the others with their high hulls, were three Newfoundland fishing-vessels drawn up on the sand at the very foot of the southern cliff, where the sea never reached except at the highest tides. From a distance their masts seemed to mingle with the branches of the trees. They were three big sailing-boats belonging to the La Houries, now laid up and peacefully rotting in the sun.

Françoise walked toward them across the shingle. On the nearest and largest flapped a festoon of tattered linen hung out to dry. This one was inhabited. A ladder with some rungs missing rested against it, and, when Françoise approached, a dog started barking on deck, running along the rail. He did not stop until she passed the worm-eaten hull and went on toward the tawny rocks of the point.

The nearest of these rocks were oddly partitioned off by concrete barriers sunk around them. From inside came a steady sound of scraping. It stopped only when Françoise shouted, "Francis!"

A head wearing a beret, with a face which split into a broad grin, appeared above the enclosure. Then it vanished again, but in a few moments the man emerged from the end of the barrier, rubbing his hands to clean them before greeting Françoise.

"Well," he cried, "so you've come to see us?"

He was a little man, wearing gaiters and a navy-blue jersey. He had one eye shut, which gave him a mischievous air of conspiracy. Taking off his beret, he shook hands with Françoise so hard that he drove her wedding-ring into her skin; but that did not stop her smiling.

"I'm so glad to see you," he went on. "I thought you'd forgotten all about us."

Françoise gazed at him gratefully, because of his delight. It was so seldom that her arrival cheered up anyone like this.

"Oh, no," she replied, "I never forget anyone."

Then she glanced toward the barriers.

67

"Still hard at work, eh?" she asked.

"Don't talk to me about it!" growled Francis, shrugging his shoulders. "They've gone nearly mad today. It's because of this early sun. They landed a whole boatload yesterday, and I simply can't keep them in. You might give me a hand, just as you did when you came here for your holidays."

He started laughing again at this memory, and his one eye sparkled. Francis was a cockle-keeper. A fishmonger in Saint-Malo brought him tons of black shell-fish from the Irish coast and poured them into his enclosures. But the sea-snails seemed to have but one instinct, and this was to escape, to scale the barriers, to get back to sea. All day and all night, when the enclosures were dry—for, when the tide came in, the guests stayed at the bottom—he had to busy himself raking them off the concrete sides up which they climbed. When he had finished at one end, he found the walls all covered with fugitives at the other. He had also to keep watch lest anyone should pick up some of them a score of yards away from his enclosures; for, despite his diligence, the biggest of them were too quick for him, and he had to make rapid rounds outside to catch them and throw them back again.

"So it's your day for calling on your aunt?" he said.

"Yes," replied Françoise.

"You won't find her in a very good temper. They've been throwing feathers into her garden again. When I called at Rocmarin, about an hour ago, she was picking them up."

Françoise nodded. Then she asked, "You still go there every morning?"

"Every morning! She never gets tired of them. For my part, I'd rather lose an eye than eat one of the beastly things."

Every morning, indeed, Francis or his wife went to Aunt Angélique's to deliver a pound of cockles. It was one of the old maid's many fads that she always ate them as an *hors-d'oeuvre*.

Glancing at the boat, on which the dog was still barking, Françoise asked, "Is Augustine on board? I must go and have a word with her."

Francis's face darkened.

"No," he replied, "she's gone to the village. We've run out of sugar. She's getting me some tobacco, too—unless she forgets it, on purpose."

He opened his one eye wide, and gazed at Françoise gravely.

"Oh," he said, "you've no idea what a fish she has become. She's much worse than she was in your time. Nowadays she never stops drinking. Of course, I know it's not much fun being on board there, spending your life there. And that reminds me, last high tide we were nearly carried away. The water came right up under us, and I've never been bumped so hard since the time I ran aground in the West Fjord. Still, that's no reason . . . It will turn out badly, one of these days. Of course, everyone has his troubles."

He gave Françoise a penetrating stare, and added, "Even you, perhaps, are not without your troubles. Though, if anyone ever deserved a pleasant life, it's certainly you. Anyway, one must make the best of things."

On board the boat, the dog barked louder than ever. Françoise turned round, and noticed that he was hopping about the hulk's deck on three paws.

"Why," she asked, "what's the matter with old Stop?"

"He broke a leg coming down the ladder a couple of months ago," replied Francis. "Since then, I have to lower him ashore in a basket. If I counted on her to do it, it would be the same as everything else. . . . Hello, here she is! Just look at her!"

A woman had just left the path and was coming across the

shingle with long, uncertain steps, which jolted her whole body.

When she came quite close, Françoise was surprised to see how hideous she had become. Her hair fell disheveled over her squinting eyes. Her complexion was the color of mud. Drunkenness parted her slack mouth and showed black gaps in her teeth. She carried a wicker basket, and talked to herself as she walked. When she caught sight of Françoise, she had to make an obvious effort before she recognized her. Then she came to a stop, distrustfully, a few feet away.

"Ah," she said, in a hoarse voice which slurred her words, "I suppose you've come about the ladder."

"About the ladder?" echoed Françoise.

Francis shrugged his shoulders; but the slut, as though offended by not being understood, went on more rudely, "Yes, about the ladder, of course. You've seen it, haven't you? Isn't it bad enough to break anyone's neck? I said so to your mother-in-law, only last week. 'You've made the dog break his leg already,' I said to her. 'And now I suppose we've got to break our necks too. You can't put on airs about giving people somewhere to live, if they can't get in and out of their home.'"

"All right, that's enough!" Francis intervened.

Head thrown back, Augustine darted a look of hatred at him, baring her teeth.

"I've got to talk to her, understand?" she retorted.

Her bleary eyes seemed to be searching around for her lost train of thought. Then she recovered it.

"Ladders! She's got any amount of them rotting away in her loft, that mother-in-law of yours. But when I asked her for one, she told me I could easily buy one with all the money I spent on drink. It's true I sometimes get drunk, but I said to your mother-in-law, 'That, Madame, is the only pleasure the poor have.' And she said to me, 'You drink enough to drive you out of your mind.' Yes, that's what she said to me, 'Drive you out of your mind.' "

The indignation which this refined reproach aroused in her amused Françoise, despite her disgust. She remembered what Aunt Angélique had once said: that insults are the more offensive the less they are understood. The old maid even declared that as a student she had borrowed her own insults from Greek metrics, and that she had nearly been assaulted by a cab-driver when she called him a "catalectic tetrameter."

"Out of your mind," the drunken woman repeated, mulishly. "Well, I'm not the only one, am I? What about her own son? Didn't she have to get him shut up?"

"Be quiet, damn it!"

Francis flung himself upon her and seized her; but she struggled and shouted, "Well, it's true, isn't it?"

Francis let his firm fists fall away from her, for the harm was done. Only then did it dawn upon Augustine: the wife of that son about whom she had spoken stood before her.

"As though you didn't know it!" she mumbled.

"Get out!"

Francis shouted at her with such fury that she was afraid. She took herself off toward the ladder.

"She doesn't know what she's saying, you know," said Francis.

Françoise gazed at him gravely.

"It's true, is it, Francis?"

From the look of surprise which he could not at once conceal, Françoise felt that he was restraining himself from repeating what his wife had said, "Didn't you know?" So she scarcely listened to his awkward, embarrassed reply, "They said at one time . . . When he went away for a rest . . . But people always talk, they always talk. . . ."

Françoise cut him short.

"That's all over now," she said.

Francis thought that she accepted the fact, that in her eyes death wiped out everything.

"Quite so," he agreed. "If we were to worry about everything that happened in the past! We've enough to worry about in the present."

"Can it be true?"

Françoise repeated it to herself as she climbed the steep path that cut into the yellow wall of the cliff, avoiding the briars which caught at her legs, the low furze-bushes which tried to entangle her.

"I'm going to find out straight away."

She hurried on as soon as the path widened, and in a few minutes came to a queer house on top of the point.

It was an old windmill, a round tower in the center of four buildings in the form of a cross. Only the tower emerged from a tangle of flowering shrubs, great bushes of rosemary, black-currant, mimosa, which drowned the square outbuildings.

Françoise rang the bell beside the massive door in the garden wall, and an old woman opened the peep-hole. Its lattice-work made funny squares of her Saint-Brieuc stringed cap, her broad, flat, weather-beaten face.

"You've come at a good time," she said. "She's as angry as the devil. They've been throwing feathers at her again."

"I know," replied Françoise. She entered the round garden.

There a tall, thin woman was busying herself with a queer job. She was dusting low rose-bushes with a feather-broom. Flakes of down were stuck to their thorns. She herself had some on her gray hair, on the shoulders of her sweater. She did not straighten herself to welcome her niece.

"Wait a minute," she said. "I'll just finish this, and then I'll be with you."

But François was in a hurry to get into the house, because her questions could not wait.

"Don't give yourself all that trouble," she replied. "The first shower of rain will get rid of that for you."

"Oh, indeed!" sneered Aunt Angélique. "Rain in this weather! Do you want me to look at this dirt on my flowers for the next fortnight? . . . Well, perhaps you're right. It's too silly. They'd be only too glad to make me pick it all off. But I'll get even with them!"

This rain of feathers on her property was a political insult, and a ritual one. Throughout Upper Brittany, at election-time, hen-feathers represented Royalist feathers, those tawny owl feathers which on days of Red triumph were carried as trophies on the ends of poles. Aunt Angélique was a stout Royalist, and, in the eyes of the Republicans, a formidable adversary. She attended political meetings, and although, as a woman, she was not entitled to speak, her loud horse-laugh dumbfounded the village orators. The Reds took their revenge by inundating her garden at night with these symbolical feathers.

She preceded Françoise into the round room which she used as a study. Shelves of white wood, full of books, many out of their proper place, rose to the ceiling. The big table, armchairs and other chairs were hidden beneath piles of booklets and pamphlets. Aunt Angélique was vice-president of the Archeological Society of Upper Brittany. She cleared a low chair of her books, and gave it a pat which raised a cloud of dust.

As she straightened herself to invite her niece to sit down, she noticed Françoise's combative air.

"What's the matter with you?" she asked, taken aback.

Her quizzical, shrewish face assumed an expression of anxious affection.

"Is it true that Luc was shut up?" demanded Françoise.

Mademoiselle de Caradeuc, who had sat down, stood up like a released spring. On her feet, she turned back into an overlong, gesticulating puppet.

"Why, of course not!" she replied. "Who ever told you that? One only shuts up madmen."

"Precisely."

"But it's you who are mad. All that happened was that, a couple of years before your marriage, your husband, like many other people, had an attack of neurasthenia, or nervous depression, and that he went to a chateau in Auvergne for a rest."

"A lunatic asylum?"

"No! A place where you take a cure of fresh air, and rest, and quiet. You see, it was a question above all of removing him from his usual surroundings, and getting him away from his mother's influence. She was absolutely besotting the boy."

Françoise rejected the explanation with a curt shake of her head.

"My mother-in-law would never have agreed to be separated from him, unless it was a matter of urgency, a dangerous case," she said. "You know that very well."

Aunt Angélique shrugged her shoulders.

"It's possible that they told her there was some danger," she replied. "But what I can assure you . . ."

"How long was he there?" Françoise interrupted.

"I don't know exactly. Eight or ten months."

"That's a long time for a rest-cure. . . . And you knew about this, when you first talked to me about him?"

Mademoiselle Caradeuc's tone of assurance was a little over-done.

"Why, of course I did. They didn't make any mystery about it. Everyone knew about it."

"No," Françoise corrected her. "I didn't know about it. I've only just heard. No one ever told me."

"And if I didn't tell you about it," exclaimed her aunt, waving her long arms, "it was because, in all good faith, it was none of my business to tell you. It was a case of one of two things. Either I believed that it might be an obstacle to marriage, and then I shouldn't have talked to you about the boy at all. Or else I didn't believe that, and then there was no reason why I should tell you about this business of his going to Auvergne. You don't say to a girl, 'I know a young man who'll just suit you; he's had nervous trouble.' That's only common sense."

At any other time, Françoise would have smiled at the idea of her aunt talking about common sense. But her frown persisted.

"Nervous trouble," she replied. "That begins with insomnia, and it ends—you know how it ends. You knew exactly what it was. . . ."

"My goodness," her aunt interrupted in her most penetrating tone, "you're taking me either for a fool or for a monster! Of course I knew. I knew before I ever thought of him for you, or you for him. I read with my own eyes a letter from the doctor who was treating him. He advised his mother to get him married. What have you got to say to that, eh?"

Sitting still, her chin uptilted on her folded hands, Françoise never took her eyes off her.

"I see. And then?"

"Well, you know your mother-in-law. You know how frantically she goes about everything she undertakes. She must find a wife for him on the spot. She ran about everywhere, looking for one, at the de Vaissés, at Maurcières, at Trézeny. She approached the Val-de-Rance girl. She approached Cécile de Pludual. She even approached Madame de Guersac's companion, that big girl Anna, who has such bad manners. And everything must be settled at once. Of course, her hurry spoiled everything. And it was then that La Hourie fell into the river, right at your feet, and that you saved his life."

"No, of course I didn't save his life. That's absurd."

"Well, all the same it was providential. The boy went off soaking wet and madly in love. . . ."

"No, he wasn't!"

The ridiculous romance which Françoise had hitherto let Aunt Angélique invent and touch up as she pleased, now exasperated her to such a point that she refused to listen to it all over again. She saw the scene once more: Luc letting her pull him ashore, without even helping himself by pushing his foot against the rock by which he had been caught. She had taken him home. Maclovie lit a big fire of furze to dry him. He talked only to explain his fall in minute detail. It was his left foot which had slipped when he moved it forward on the rock. He would not have fallen if, at this moment, the little ridge on which he was resting his right foot had not given way. Even when he slipped, he could have recovered his balance if he had not held on to his rod with his right hand. It was only when he fell that he let go of it.

Then, still steaming, he stood up.

"I must go," he said, "or my mother will be getting anxious. What time is it?"

His wrist-watch had stopped when it got wet.

When Françoise told him that it was half past twelve, he got into a panic, and she lent him her bicycle so that he could pick up his car more quickly. He did not thank her for it, but he said, "I owe you my life." This amused her at the time, but now it infuriated her by its stupid exaggeration.

Aunt Angélique must have gone on talking hard during these few moments when Françoise, for her part, was back on the banks of the river. Mademoiselle had even started walking up and down as she spoke, which always meant that she had an idea. Now she stopped in front of her niece to let go her fine argument at close quarters.

"You reproach me with not telling you about that silly business. But what about you? Did you tell them about your sister? Or did they ever say anything to you about it? But they knew all about it. Your mother-in-law referred to it in my presence, but only to say that it would not stop her for a moment, and that she did not want you to have any idea that she knew. What about that?"

Françoise stood up, distracted.

"Why, can't you see that she was delighted about it? That shameful story played straight into her hands. She had closed the doors of all the chateaux against herself. She couldn't even buy that girl Anna at Le Mesnil. She thought she was for sale, but Anna wasn't selling herself, because she knew what kind of marriage she would be making. She told me so, or next door to it. But when she found a girl with no family, with no money, a girl whose sister had killed herself because she got in the family way with a quarryman—that, as you put it, was providential! A girl like that wouldn't make difficulties. She wouldn't bargain. She could be got cheap, to be handed over body and soul to a maniac whom no one else would have."

Mademoiselle de Caradeuc raised her long arms in horror.

"That's no way to talk! He's dead, you know."

Françoise sat down again, burying her face in her hands. Conquered by her Breton respect for the dead, she murmured, "That's true. Forgive me!"

But she went on, "All the same, that's what my mother-in-law thought. That's what everyone thought when they heard about my marriage. And I never knew!"

That gave Aunt Angélique her chance to sneer.

"And why should you worry about what fools and rogues thought? That's not like you."

She took Françoise by the arm and returned to the only one of her arguments which had struck home.

"No one has any right to call the dead to account, you know, because they're no longer here to defend themselves. . . . Come along, let's have lunch. . . . Who told you all this?"

When Françoise told her that it was Francis's wife, Mademoiselle de Caradeuc was triumphant.

"The rambling of a drunken woman! You swallow all that, and then you come here and make a scene! You let me spend my breath explaining and proving things to you, and then you say, 'Augustine told me.' The least one can do is quote proper authority. . . . Well, that's finished with. Come to table."

Françoise let herself be borne along by her aunt's flow of words. They deafened her, but still they kept away for the moment thoughts which would come back to her all too soon.

"And what about the Queen Mother?" asked Aunt Angélique. "How's she behaving? Eating you alive, just a bit at a time, eh? My poor girl, she's been doing it for the last fifty years. At the Sacré-Coeur, she used to pull out our hair, one at a time, to make wigs for her dolls. And she did it in the chapel, too, so that we couldn't cry out! After that, it was her husband's turn,

La Hourie VI, a fellow who descended from the corsair just as you descend a long staircase when you slip—on his backside! There's one thing that always surprised me, though, and that is that La Hourie was thin when he married and fat when he died. But he was such a fool—I can say that, because you never knew him and so he was never really your father-in-law—that he never realized a twentieth part of all the spiteful things she did to him."

She heaped her niece's plate with such a large helping of cake that Françoise protested. Mademoiselle de Caradeuc did not even hear her.

"Still, make what you can of it," she went on, "she never managed to get herself thoroughly hated, because she was as capable of the most delicate attentions as of the most exquisitely dirty tricks. And one of them on top of the other! She'd kiss you furiously, she'd force everything she possessed upon you, while you were still making faces over the pinch she'd just given you. You know that, of course?"

Françoise nodded.

"Yes, she hasn't changed," declared her aunt. "So you're dazed. You don't understand it. You let yourself be taken in over and over again because you feel as convinced when she kisses you as when she pinches you. But, in the long run, pinches leave more mark on you than kisses. And, along with that, she's got a calculating machine clamped right down inside her. So, in connection with her loss—and your loss—she has a way of keeping count of her troubles, for fear lest she should be robbed of a single one of them, which might discourage Our Lady the Helper. Isn't that true?"

"Yes, it's quite true."

Aunt Angélique laughed.

"Ah, how well I know her! When I advised you to marry

that poor boy, I knew what kind of mother-in-law you'd find her. But I was sure you'd have the last word. You were just the daughter-in-law she needed—a counterpoise. She might nod right or left; but that wouldn't make you budge, and she's always been afraid of characters like that. . . . But who could ever imagine that poor La Hourie VII, after managing to fall into the water once while he was shrimping, would go off and get himself drowned like that off Lapland, or wherever it was? . . . Well, what are you going to do? I don't mean to-morrow, of course, but for the future in general? Are you going on living with her?"

"No," said Françoise. "I couldn't do that now."

The curt tone in which she replied made Mademoiselle de Caradeuc look up. She recognized the rebel face of the Fraôs, which she called their "1626 face," for it was in that year that one Bernard du Fraô, a friend of Chalais, sprang at Richelieu, dagger drawn, on a staircase in the Louvre.

Scratching the table with her fingernail, she said, shyly, "Whatever you decide, I needn't tell you that this house is always open to you."

She waited for a reply, but Françoise said nothing, and she went on, "You haven't got any money, of course, have you? You were married in accordance with the rule of separate maintenance?"

"Yes."

"Of course, that would be one way for your mother-in-law to keep you under her thumb. So all you have is your manor and your two little farms at Le Fraô and your mill? Altogether, that ought to bring you in about eight thousand francs. Counting repairs and taxes, you've got about six thousand left."

"Yes."

80

"I could give you as much again. It would only be an advance, because I'm leaving everything I have to you. But I won't offer it to you, because you'd refuse it. So the only thing left for you is to give lessons. You don't have to know what you teach, and you could find a few backward children whom even the priests won't have. I'll bet that's what you've been thinking about?"

"About what?"

"About that! Haven't you been listening to me?"

"No."

"Are you still thinking about that business?"

"No, I'm not!"

Françoise stood up as she spoke, so impatiently, so harshly, that Aunt Angélique realized that she was shutting her out from her agony. The knowledge made her big mouth twist with distress.

Françoise went into the study. When Mademoiselle de Caradeuc followed her there, she found Françoise holding a carved stone which she had picked up from a shelf. It looked like the head of a woman in torture, lips drawn back, nose broken, skull notched with deep cuts.

Aunt Angélique regarded it as the mutilated head of a statue of Serena, a local goddess of her own invention, whose traces she had been following up for some time, and who was, according to her, the last of the sirens. It was, she declared, Serena who had given her name to Saint-Servan: Ser-Fanum. The Welsh and Irish monks of the fifth century had turned the siren into a saint, in accordance with their usual practice of taking over local deities and canonizing them. All the time that Mademoiselle de Caradeuc did not devote to the stout defense of religion she spent in knocking the regional saints off their pedestals in this way.

81

When she entered the study, Françoise turned round, holding out the head.

"How are you getting on with your memoir about this?" she asked.

Aunt Angélique looked at her reproachfully.

"Why do you ask me about that now?"

"Because I suppose it interests you, of course!"

There was such an intent to hurt in Françoise's tone that the old maid took her by the arm and led her gently toward the door.

"You'd better go, my dear. . . ."

FRANÇOISE trembled with indignation CHAPTER FIVE all night long.

How they had fooled her, how they had swindled her, how they had made a mockery of her! In a rage, as she went back over the days and the nights of her marriage, she recalled strange aberrations of Luc's, crazy fancies which had astonished or disgusted her. So that was what it was! She remembered odd questions which her mother-in-law had asked, precautions which she had recommended. But nothing had enlightened her! She had taken them to be decent people. "The wife of a madman!" She said it out loud in the dark. Then a violent resentment made her sit up cursing in her big white bed. A thought which yesterday she would have rejected with horror stirred within her. It was a blessing that he was dead!

She did not sleep until dawn, and what awakened her when it was broad daylight was an agonizing feeling that she had become ugly while she was asleep. The impression was so strong that she put her hands to her cheeks. Then, together with the light and the sounds of morning that came into her room, one fact stamped itself on her mind.

Everyone—Annette who was ringing the bell for breakfast, Grioul whom she could hear steadily raking the gravel, the two housemaids moving about in the linen-cupboard above her, everyone in the village, everyone in the chateau—all of them believed that she had sold herself. All of them believed that, for the sake of La Hourie's wealth, she had surrendered herself to this half-man, sullied by a madhouse worse than by the stigma of prison.

Suddenly she thought about Maurière, whom she had forgotten ever since she had heard Augustine's words. Was not what he had dared to do a sign that he, too, knew about Luc? A madman's wife might be expected to put up with any insult, any liberty.

As she passed before the mirror in its carved frame inlaid on the door, she stopped. As a girl, she had often amused herself by playing a strange game in front of a mirror. She stared her reflection steadily in the eyes, until she achieved a kind of splitting of herself, a sort of separation from her image. She had boasted about this feat one day to a priest. "But that's dangerous!" he exclaimed, without explaining why. Was it because the hypnosis this contemplation induced gave her a sense of discernment about herself which was sometimes very disturbing? Or was it because it evoked this besetting double of hers, which sometimes seemed to be out of her control, reappeared every time she passed the mirror, and ended by creating the obsession of an inexorably parallel presence?

Now she ran into her refound reflection. She had forgotten this game of hers for years. She looked at herself in a mirror nowadays not for her own sake, but as women always do, in order to judge herself from the viewpoint of others, to see herself as she wanted to be seen. Again, like all women, all she studied was the details of her clothes and her face, apart from the final glance over her shoulder which swept right down her figure.

This time, she saw her reflection move, as though it shunned inspection. But she brought herself back into focus firmly. She studied herself sternly, trying to discover in her appearance

84

some explanation of Maurière's insulting boldness. No, neither her black dress, nor the look in her eyes, nor her face, which she did not make up, could have misled the fellow. Françoise, like every woman, had her own precise catalogue of feminine types, neatly ranging from the provocative to the plain and retiring. She saw now that she had exactly the appearance which she thought she had, and no man could make any mistake about it. She was sure of that.

If Maurière had behaved like a cad, it must have been because he assumed, on account of her past, that she would not be easily shocked. With a woman who had submitted to the kisses of a madman, one should be able to hurry things up. All at once she despised Maurière, as though she had just learned something infamous about him.

As for herself, she was going away—without saying why. Was she to proclaim, "I know all about it. I'm going away?" No! Her shame was her own, and she was not going to make an exhibition of it. Why should she make accusations or give vent to reproaches? Did you reproach a wild beast when it tore up living prey for its young? You did no such thing. You ran away from it, while you had time. And now that it was too late . . .

It was not until afternoon that Françoise found a chance to tell her mother-in-law about her decision. The April sun was already turning yellow in the still air. The tree-trunks rose straight into the bright green of their young leaves, shot with chrome. A magpie pecked on the lawn. Madame la Hourie had ordered wicker chairs to be carried out on to the south terrace, the one which overlooked the French-style garden. The vista of flower-beds and trimmed yews was bounded by a gorse hedge bordering a field of colza. Thus Brittany invaded imitation Versailles at one end.

"It's nice weather today," said Madame la Hourie, as she sat down.

For the first time in months she seemed to realize that there was an outside world.

"Nice weather, isn't it?" she repeated.

Thus called upon, Françoise nodded assent.

Annette made her appearance, her face looking brighter, as though all this light had cheered her up. She carried the work-table. She was wearing white linen shoes, just as she did at the height of summer.

"I wanted to give my feet a holiday," she said, when her mistress expressed surprise. Only Madame la Hourie smiled at her reply.

Then Grioul, dragging his clogs along the gravel, made his way to the terrace.

"The rose-bushes have just arrived from Saint-Servan," he announced.

As a rule, Françoise herself inspected the bushes. She loved to read their names on the little yellow labels. These stems of thorny wood which were called "Belle of Baltimore," "King's Rose," or "Princess of Bagdad" delighted her with their promise. It was she who divided them among the flower-beds in accordance with their color. But this time she dismissed Grioul.

"Arrange them as you like," she said.

"Aren't you going to choose them?" asked Madame la Hourie, in surprise.

"No."

When the gardener had gone, Françoise said, "I'm going away, Mamma."

"Going away?" Madame la Hourie repeated.

"Yes."

"For good?"

"Yes . . . I've been intending to tell you so for some time."

As a rule, annoyance on Madame la Hourie's part grew at once into anger. Her face trembled. A nervous twitch ran across it, always in the same way. It started at the left corner of her mouth, pulled it sideways, then pinched her nostrils in an indignant indrawing of breath, and finally proceeded to close her right eye. Her thick lips barely tightened. Then she bent her head so low that the roll of fat under her chin sank into her black bodice.

"I can't say that this surprises me," she said, as though she were speaking to herself. "For weeks I've had the impression that you had become a stranger."

She raised her head and looked at Françoise.

"I won't ask you where you're going," she went on. "No doubt you settled everything with Angélique yesterday. When are you thinking of going?"

"As soon as possible."

"Any time is possible if you've made up your mind not to bother about anything else. I'm not asking anything for myself, you needn't think that. I shall stay alone with my memories. Fundamentally, there won't be any difference. But there's his memory, there's his name you bear. So you owe me at least time to announce your decision and get our friends to accept it. Is that too much to ask?"

"Settle the date yourself."

"Easter is ten days off. What do you say to Whitsun?"

"All right, Whitsun."

"That will make more than a year. . . . The law requires only three hundred days of widowhood."

Madame la Hourie's sarcasm was to be divined only from

the sudden softening of her voice, the conciliatory tone which blurred it. Françoise felt that her determination to keep silent was on the point of giving way. She stood up.

"I'm going down to the warren," she said.

The rabbit-runs plunged into the roots of a great cedar. As a rule, Françoise approached this corner of the park only with care. She was always interested in the life of the rabbits which swarmed there. Without putting them on the alert, she had learned how to reach a bush from which she could watch their brief frolics, their swaying trot, the signals of their mobile ears, the comical gravity with which they sat down. But this time she took no precautions about her arrival. She did not even notice the swift panic it caused.

"Announce your decision, get it accepted . . ." That, she reflected, would be easy enough. It would take only a few nods, an air of reticence, and that venomous indulgence whose formulas she could guess in advance. "I can't ask her to sacrifice herself to a memory." Or else, "Françoise has some very fine qualities, but one can't expect her to feel certain things. I envy her sometimes. She has a strong character."

Then, when Madame la Hourie had gone, someone would say, "Her daughter-in-law went to Plangomeur only for the sake of the money she could make there. Now she's going off with it." No one would believe that she was going away as poor as she came.

Two rings of the bell sounding through the leaves startled her. Two rings: that must be for her. It was Maurière.

All day long she had hoped he would not come. It was an unconfessed hope, such as you reproach yourself for cherishing, but whose uprooting nevertheless hurts your soul in the depths where it lay hidden. No matter, since he, too, had returned to the attack, she would repel him, tired though she was.

Yet she turned her back on the summons and walked along paths cut through the brushwood to the spur of rock at the end of the park. The engineers' work was no longer noisy. The posts were erected, though still without wires, and the cube of the transformer showed white behind a screen of young firs. Maurière had kept his word. He had done his best to hide it.

Françoise did not notice it. She went straight to three men busy around a big drum of copper wire, and said to the eldest, "When you see Monsieur Maurière, would you tell him for me that there's no need for him to come back to the chateau?"

"But he's just gone there," the man replied.

"Has he? Well, there's no occasion. Tell him that what he did yesterday is enough. He'll know what I mean. But be sure to tell him that the message is from me."

"Very well, Madame."

Françoise went back slowly through the wood. So he had dared to pursue her even to her home. "I'll come tomorrow. . . . Talk to you alone. . . ." And he had come, because he sensed around her that loneliness which is scented by any man on the hunt, and fires him to such a point that, in his caddishness, he cannot distinguish between a woman who wants him and one who does not. It was because he had taken her for one of the women to whom he was doubtless in the habit of addressing himself that she had forbidden him, and through one of his workmen, to come to Plangomeur.

"Why, where have you been, Françoise?" asked Madame la Hourie. "The engineer has been here asking for you. What is it now?"

"Nothing," replied Françoise. "I've just been down to

where they're working. He only came to say good-bye. They've nearly finished."

"And a good riddance, too! They've done quite enough damage."

A few moments later, Annette reappeared.

"The chief engineer has been here," she said.

"I know," replied Françoise.

"He said he'd come back."

"No, he won't. I've been to see the men myself. There's no need for him to come back."

"Well, he'll be no loss. The sooner he takes all his machinery away, the better. . . . Oh, I meant to tell you. The cat's had kittens. Six of them, she's had. They're in the barn."

"All right, I'll go there."

It was Françoise who drowned newborn kittens. She had insisted on doing so ever since a day when, entering the washhouse, she heard faint mewing coming from a slop-pail with its lid closed. She uncovered it and saw four kittens, their hides like rats', sleek and black, swimming with their eyes shut and their pink, shapeless little paws scratching at the smooth sides of the enamel bucket. The sight made her angry. Annette or Grioul just threw them into a bucket of water like that, and then took themselves off. The kittens, straight from their warm nest, swam in the cold water, mewing faintly but shrilly, until they came to the end of their strength. At full stretch in the water, they looked horribly long, Françoise plunged her arms into the bucket, and held the cluster of living bodies under the water until she could no longer feel them moving beneath her fingers. Ever since then, she herself had drowned all the kittens; but she ate no dinner those evenings.

"Six to be drowned again!" exclaimed Madame la Hourie.

"Why, it seems endless! And they always leave the job to you."

"Yes," replied Françoise, "I told them. Then at least I'm sure that it's done quickly."

Madame la Hourie's lips twitched at the mere idea of the execution.

"I'd rather be killed myself," she said. "Just imagine feeling them struggling all warm in your hands, and then plunging them under the water! Oh, no!"

"Would you rather let them suffer for hours?" retorted Françoise. "It's terrible how much life they have in them."

Madame la Hourie made repeated signs of approval with head and hands.

"You're quite right," she said. "I'm just admiring you for being able to do it."

When Françoise left the barn, her teeth still clenched to keep back the nausea of her drowning, Grioul was in the drive raking away the marks of the last trucks.

Holy Week, with its emotional atmosphere to which Françoise had always been keenly responsive, imposed a truce upon her. It forced her to escape from herself. On Holy Thursday she had to decorate the "tomb." On Good Friday she had to be present at the Stations of the Cross and the Passion sermon. On Saturday, after the long service, she had to put flowers on the altars for Sunday.

She hoped that these days would mean a halt, during which she could store up strength before setting off in life again all alone. The priest to whom she went for her Easter confession reminded her that the Church, in her hierarchy of saints, places widows immediately after virgins.

For her penance, he imposed upon her reading of Saint Paul's *First Epistle to Timothy*. "Now she that is a widow indeed, and desolate, trusteth in God, and continueth in supplications and prayers night and day. But she that liveth in pleasure is dead while she liveth. . . . Well reported of for good works, if she have brought up children, if she have lodged strangers, if she have washed the saints' feet, if she have relieved the afflicted."

Was this in itself the answer to the questions which presented themselves to her about her life, about her future? She had prayed that Communion on Easter morning would enlighten her.

Then she read further on, beyond the Apostle's savage portrayal of wanton widows, idle, tattlers and busybodies, going about from house to house, speaking things which they ought not, and his imperious counsel surprised and disturbed her. "I will therefore that the younger women marry, bear children, guide the house, give none occasion to the adversary to speak reproachfully."

The younger women!

As she closed the Bible, she said to herself, "I'm only twenty-five!"

The calm which she awaited on Easter morning, the peace for which she had rashly set that date, did not come to her.

Madame la Hourie, for her part, carried away from Holy Week a torture which beset her day and night. She had always refused to pray for her son. It was a dogma with her that Luc was among those predestined to Heaven. In any case, would not his terrible death have compensated, and more than compensated, for any failings he may have had?

But the Lenten preacher, in a retreat sermon in which he had dealt with duties toward the dead, had attacked those presumptuous people who, assured of the salvation of a loved one, neglected to pray for him.

"Dare you think that the scales of God are the same as your own? Dare you think that He ratifies in Heaven the judgments which your pride or your weakness have led you to pass upon the works of those you have loved? They may be in travail now, as they look upon you lulled in the mistaken assurance which robs them of your help, and reduces them to the rank of the most abandoned of souls."

Immediately after the sermon, Madame la Hourie had hastened to the vestry to order Masses for the repose of Luc's soul. She scanned the rector's notebook, just as though it were a farm-book, and put down the name of La Hourie on all the empty pages. Back at Plangomeur, she reproached herself vehemently in Françoise's presence. A whole year! For a whole year her son had been suffering through her fault, when, from the very first day, she could have mobilized the potent strength of prayer, which would have spared him the torments of Purgatory. The thought of them ravaged her. She besought her daughter-in-law to join with her in his deliverance.

"But I've prayed for him from the very first day," replied Françoise.

It was quite true. Never, even at her worst moments, had she failed in this duty.

Finding herself thus outrun, thus supplanted, Madame la Hourie could not hide a wretched grimace of envy. Then she murmured, "You must go on praying."

But she never mentioned these prayers for Luc again. She did not even tell Françoise the dates of the Masses which she had ordered. She went to them alone, at seven o'clock in the morning, secretly.

On Low Tuesday, she came into the little drawing room

where Françoise was working, all in a fluster. Aunt Angélique had asked Françoise to copy out for her some documents about the corsair, and Françoise had accepted this task with pleasure. Madame la Hourie handed her a letter.

"Read this, please," she said. "For my part, I'm wondering whether I quite understand it. It's from Souchard, the ship-owner. He tells me that one of his trawler captains, Captain Gennebault, is coming to see me tomorrow. It's something to do with 'information' he's got for us. But what information can it be?"

Françoise read the letter:

"He will give you some slight information which he picked up on the Murmansk coast. I have hesitated for some time about sending it to you and awakening painful memories. Then I said to myself that a name, a date, little though they may be, might perhaps be more helpful to you than nothing at all. If I am mistaken, please forgive me."

"So," Madame la Hourie went on, "they've heard something about the wreck?"

Françoise referred to the letter again.

"Not much, apparently. 'A name, a date.' He says, 'Some slight information.'"

Madame la Hourie shook her head.

"I know, but he also says, 'picked up on the Murmansk coast.' Does that mean that someone saw the wreck, that someone knows where the ship went down? Where's the Murmansk coast? You don't know? Have we got an atlas?"

"I don't know, but there'll be something in the *Encyclopaedia*."

"Come and have a look, will you?"

Françoise followed her mother-in-law to Luc's room. Madame la Hourie squatted down in front of the low bookcase. Twice she made a mistake about the right volume.

"Murmansk? Let me see, that will be under 'H—Mel,' won't it? No, of course, it's 'Mel—Poz.' Look it up for me, will you?"

Françoise read aloud, "Coast low and marshy. Intense cold, reaching 40 degrees below zero. Polar vegetation, lichen and moss. Principal town: Murmansk. Fishing and fur-trading."

"Is that all?"

"Yes."

"But can't we find anything else—some book about geography or travels?"

Françoise discovered *Around the World* in two volumes, two thick, dusty volumes.

"Let me dust them for you," she suggested.

"No, no!" replied Madame la Hourie. "Give them to me!"

She carried them off hastily, an armful of them, clasped to her stomach.

Captain Gennebault arrived at three o'clock the next afternoon. Sitting at a French window in the drawing room, Madame la Hourie had been watching out for him for the last hour and a half. When she caught sight of him at the end of the drive, a short, thick-set man, wearing a light raincoat and a new felt hat, she stood up, and then sat down again.

"My legs won't hold me," she confessed.

She breathed heavily as she watched him coming, her shoulders rising and falling.

When he came to the edge of the tulip-bed, the captain slowed down and stopped. He liked looking at flowers; he had been away from them so long. But Madame la Hourie tapped nervously with her fingertips on the arm of her chair.

"What on earth is he doing?"

As though he had heard her, the captain set off again, and he climbed the steps so quickly that he rang the bell before Françoise, who was folding her knitting, had managed to put her last ball of wool away in her work-basket.

He came in, gave a keen look round the drawing room, saw the wife and the mother together, and hesitated. It had always been to the wives of the men he had lost in the course of his career that he addressed himself first, and for a moment his eyes lingered on Françoise. Then Madame la Hourie came forward.

"Captain Gennebault, isn't it?"

He turned toward her.

"Yes, Madame."

He had now got his bearings, and, when he sat down, it was toward the old lady that he looked.

"Our friend, Monsieur Souchard, told us you were coming," she said. "I gather you picked up some information about . . . about the *Entreprenant*."

Gennebault settled himself in his chair to gain solid support.

"Very little, unfortunately, Madame," he replied. "It was like this. Last August, in the White Sea, we found ourselves fishing close to a Soviet trawler. Funny fellows they were, too. They had women on board as cooks, and they burst into song at any moment. Well, one of them was a net-mender who spoke a little French. He had been at Mailly Camp during the war. It was from him that I heard that they had sighted the *Entreprenant*, the very day before the cyclone. But she was much farther west than had been thought: twenty miles northeast of the Ponoi estuary, off Donka Bay. As you know, she was believed to have been lost much farther east. The Gulf of Tanovsk was mentioned."

Madame la Hourie found it hard not to show her impatience.

96

What did all these names mean to her? Was this all he had to say?

"It's not surprising that they should have been farther west," Gennebault went on. "They set off very early, for, thanks to the exceptionally mild winter, the fishing season started a good month sooner than usual. Still, they were hampered by the break-up of the ice. Their last radio message said so. For a time, indeed, their loss was attributed to collision with an iceberg. I assume that Captain Halluin tried to fish all the same, and then, about the twenty-fifth, he decided to make for clear water, to the west of the Murmansk coast. The Russian ship sighted him on the twenty-seventh in Donka Bay, taking soundings. It was there that the cyclone fell upon him."

The captain's wave of his hand indicated that, from that moment, he gave the *Entreprenant* up for lost.

"They must have tried to put to sea to ride out the storm. But, in my opinion, for some reason we shall never know, perhaps a breakdown of the engines or the steering-gear, they couldn't get out to sea, and they were driven into the shoals of the bay. It's all rocks and marshes about there. The Russian, too, thought that they must have been driven southward out of control, onto the coastal reefs. To make sure, at the end of the season, when I got back to Murmansk to fuel, I made inquiries, and I heard that some Samoyeds had found wreckage in the marshes of the peninsula: a barrel, some partition planks, and, above all, the forepart of a shattered whaleboat with a case of biscuits stowed away in it. This case bore the mark, still legible, of the Saint-Servan factory. It belonged to the *Entreprenant*, all right. In any event, that case proved that at one time they contemplated getting the boats away, with food on board. Did they even succeed in launching the whaleboat? I don't believe it. Any boat would have been overturned and smashed

97

up, with the sea that was running. That cyclone lasted two days, the Russian told me, and it cleared their decks. Even if the *Entreprenant's* crew were able to launch their boats, they wouldn't have got far."

"Why not?" demanded Madame la Hourie, pale as death.

Gennebault raised his right hand, and dropped it on his left with a little slap.

"Because, Madame, in a situation in which a trawler like the *Entreprenant* couldn't stand the storm, you can imagine that a boat would sink like a paper-boat. It would be capsized, carried away, smashed to bits. Besides, the proof that it all happened very suddenly is that they hadn't even time to send out an S. O. S. Their aerial must have been carried away first of all."

Françoise listened motionless. Madame la Hourie sobbed. The captain stood up.

"I didn't want to come," he said, in a husky tone of voice. "What could I tell you? Just that they were lost, between the twenty-eighth and the thirtieth, farther west than had been supposed. Whether it happened here or there, it doesn't make much difference to you, does it?"

Madam la Hourie looked up. A tear trembled at the end of her chin, and another ran down her nose. But her fists shook, and it was angrily that she cried, "But after all, in a bay, so close to the coast, how did it happen that no one was saved? So close, and still no one!"

The captain shook his head.

"It's better to keep away from the bays in those parts in bad weather, Madame. They're all reefs with teeth like saws stuck in the mud. If you run onto them, they cut the bottom out of you. I don't know any coast that's worse, apart from the quicksands in Iceland. Halluin was a good sailor, and he would have done all he could, and more. But, when the cyclone caught him in that spot, he must have known at once that it was hopeless."

He waited, sitting straight in his chair, until the sobs that shook Madame la Hourie were a little easier. Then he stood up and bowed to her. Madame la Hourie looked up and stared at him with odd intensity, as though he had only just entered the room. Then, all at once, she passed in front of her daughter-in-law to show him out.

When he was in the hall, near the door, in a low voice, like that in which one questions a doctor out of the patient's ear-shot, she asked, hurriedly, "So it is impossible to suppose that anyone may have reached land, that anyone may have been saved?"

Gennebault shook his head again.

"At sea, Madame, nothing is absolutely impossible. The same wave may drown one man and save another. But, after more than a year, and given the circumstances of the wreck, the question unfortunately cannot arise. My respects, Madame!"

He opened the door slowly, stopped on the threshold for a final bow, and went down the steps, carefully settling his new hat, a Tyrolean hat stamped with a little pheasant's feather.

Madame la Hourie came back and sat down again at the French window. Her hands folded in her lap, she watched the captain walking calmly away along the green drive. Françoise started knitting again; but sometimes, without moving her head, she looked up and furtively studied her mother-in-law. Never had she seen her face so poignant in its immobility. As a rule, sorrow kept her face working ceaselessly. She made sudden grimaces, her features tautened and then suddenly relaxed again, and always she had that persistent air of being

on the hunt, as though she had lost something instead of someone. But during these last few minutes her heavy face had remained set in a grief so tragic that Françoise was touched by it.

"I ought to go and kiss her," she said to herself. But she reflected that she would be giving only a stranger's kiss for a
sorrow which she had refused to share. Such a kiss would simply be an insult. She bent lower and went on knitting.

"Why did he come, Françoise?" asked Madame la Hourie.
"It would have been better not to know anything about it."

Françoise nodded assent.

Madame la Hourie went on, "If they had time to launch the
boats, they must have known that they were going to be
drowned."

The voice of Luc's mother broke as she spoke. Françoise
realized that she was living through the terrible scene which
she herself had so often imagined: Luc taken by surprise by
the stampede, his frenzied panic, his frantic prayers, his shouts
of protest against death, his nightmare cries of "Mamma!"
smothered by the water. Once all this horror had awakened
Françoise at night, her heart pounding.

During the next few days, she was surprised that Madame
la Hourie made no mention of the captain's cruel visit. She
merely seemed to be possessed by a sudden urge toward movement, which drove her all over the house at any hour of the
day, giving all kinds of orders, inventing all kinds of jobs.

Though she realized that her mother-in-law was hoping to
escape from her torment in this way, Françoise watched her
making herself busy with suppressed irritation. Her breathless moving about broke that monotony which shortened the
hours so nicely. There were plenty of hours left before Whitsun.

To get through them calmly, Françoise counted upon her

long apprenticeship to boredom. At Le Fraô, as she watched the river flow by; at the Moulin de Rance, seated at her father's bedside; at Plangomeur itself, beside her mother-in-law while she was still prostrated, she had endured the unbroken emptiness of day after day. She must go on doing so, here or elsewhere. Days which would pass with no color, no hope! They would touch one another end to end, for from the morning she would await the night and sleep, which would come at its appointed time, after all the hours in which nothing had happened. She might live like that for a very long time, almost eternally, perhaps.

One afternoon when she had sent Grioul to the village, he came back at the quickened pace which meant that he had important news. She went down the drive to meet him.

Even before he reached her, he exclaimed, "You know the engineer who came here to put up the line?"

"Yes, what about him?"

"Well, he's run into a plane-tree, just outside the school. He was avoiding a little girl who ran almost under his wheels. I've just seen his car. The boot is jammed into the bonnet. He was picked up ten yards off. When I got there, the Saint-Servan ambulance was taking him away."

"He's not dead?"

As she spoke, Françoise flung her arms out in a spontaneous gesture which demanded a reply at once, whatever it might be. Taken by surprise, Grioul stared at her as he answered.

"I don't think so. Though he's lucky that he's not, after a smash like that! Of course, he was unconscious. Well, for my part, I'm not surprised. He was always a break-neck fellow. Always game for anything. They never did any blasting in the rocks over there without his setting the fuse himself. They never felled a tree without his striking the final blows of the ax. He wasn't obliged to do it. He did it for fun. A dare-devil, I say!"

When Françoise got back to the house, she met her mother-in-law in the hall.

"The engineer who put up the line here has just had a bad car smash," she said. "I'm going to telephone to ask how he is."

She saw how surprised Madame la Hourie looked, but she did not deign to slacken her pace.

In the office she found Marie, the youngest of the house-maids, polishing the floor. She waved her to the door.

"I want to telephone."

Once alone, she asked for the number of the hospital. During the few moments' wait, while the telephone buzzed at her ear, she imagined Maurière, full length and all blackened, lying sprawled in the road, arms flung out, face down in the dust.

"Who's speaking?" asked a voice.

The question found Françoise unready for it. It was she who was there to ask questions.

She thought of hiding behind her mother-in-law's name, and saying, "I'm speaking for Madame la Hourie, at Plango-meur." But she remembered that this was her own name too. So she simply said, "A friend of Monsieur Maurière's—the accident case who's just been brought in. Have the doctors seen him? What do they say?"

There was a silence, a long one. Then the voice which had hesitated about replying to this nameless woman came through with cold clarity.

"The doctors haven't given their opinion yet."

"Is he badly hurt?"

There was a pause before the voice replied, "No, not obviously."

"Are they afraid of internal injuries?"

There was a heavier silence.

"Possibly."

"Has he recovered consciousness?"

"Yes."

"Then there's no immediate danger."

"Not immediate."

Françoise hoped for a moment that she would be granted
the boon of further details; but there was nothing more than
the sound of a shell in her ear. She was familiar with the distrustful discretion of nursing sisters. She knew how skilled
they were at shielding the silence, the suave quiet of their hos-
pitals, against the curiosity, the anxiety, of the outside world.

"Thank you, Sister."

She hung up the receiver.

Then, still standing at the telephone, she reflected, "I said
a friend. I refused to give my name. Perhaps she took me for
his mistress."

This thought, which five minutes earlier would have made
her burn with shame, reassured her despite herself. The nun's
reticence might be explained by her suspicion. Perhaps it did
not mean that there was no hope for Maurière.

"WELL," said Aunt Angélique, as they left the little cemetery, "there's another laid to rest!"

Turning to Françoise, who held her head away lest she should show her tears, she went on, "The very last time I saw him, he talked to me about you. He said, 'What I like about her is that she's proud without being haughty.' What do you think of that, eh? Just imagine a poor snail-gatherer being capable of thinking a thing like that!"

Françoise, for her part, was thinking about something else. She could still hear drunken Augustine, at their last meeting, shouting that Luc had had to be shut up. She could still see old Francis springing to silence her, and his distressed face afterward.

As they walked on, Mademoiselle de Caradeuc said, "I had a frightful thought at the church just now. I said to myself, 'Suppose that old trollop wasn't telling lies? Suppose it were true that she gave him only a little push? Suppose he only made that a pretext to let himself go overboard, because he was tired of it all?' That would be still more sad."

"When did you hear about it?" asked Françoise.

"Why, right afterward! She came and hammered at my door, at eleven o'clock at night. I hadn't gone to bed yet; I was working. She said to me, 'He's just fallen into the water!' Her fright had made her more or less sober. She told me that the tide had come up under the boat, as it does every month, that they had had a row on deck, that he had tried to strike her, and that, as they struggled, unintentionally she had made him

104

fall overboard. He went down at once, and in the dark she could see nothing more. Just imagine it! That woman coming back soused to the gills, shouting, shameless! And then the fight in the dark, with the sea thumping against the old timbers! She fights like an old hooligan, with her fists and her head. I've seen her. She kept on saying, 'I only gave him a little push.' Suppose that were true? I said to her, 'That's a question for the police.' I locked her up safe, I telephoned, and two hours later the police arrived and took her away. Then, the next morning, I crossed the river, and I called on the Minquiers. Yes, the Minquiers . . ."

Françoise had raised her eyebrows. The Minquiers, father and son, who fished for sand-eels, were the center of the local Communist cell. The father was a candidate at every election. Every time he collected only a score of votes, but he never got tired of trying.

Aunt Angélique went on, "I said to them, 'You know what I think about you, don't you? But you know the river better than anyone else. Francis is in it. Go and fish him out for me, and don't leave him to the crabs.' They said, 'All right. We will.' And, before midday, they found him, below Jouvente."

They walked on for a time in silence. Then Mademoiselle de Caradeuc stopped dead.

"And what about the dog?" she asked. "I thought about the dog at once. What was he doing all the time? Whom did he side with? Why didn't he spring at that woman's throat, while she was pushing Francis overboard? If animals are just going to fold their paws nowadays, things have come to a pretty pass!"

When they were back at Rocmarin, Françoise remarked, "You won't get your snails any more."

Mademoiselle de Caradeuc shrugged her shoulders.

105

"Why, I never ate one of them, my dear!" she replied. "It just meant a little profit for Francis. It helped him buy his tobacco. Besides, it amused him so much to think that I was capable of swallowing a plateful of them every day for the last ten years. We should never deprive people of the small pleasure of thinking that we're crazy—I mean when they're nice people, of course. And now about you. You came in your car, didn't you? Good, that will give us time for a bit of a talk. It's only half past three. I've been thinking about you, you know, ever since you last came. I've been considering all you told me, all about your plans."

Françoise did not remember having said much, but her aunt went on, "I've had two ideas about you, one bad and one good. Let's take the bad one first. As you won't stay with your mother-in-law, and you won't come here or accept any money from me, naturally you're thinking about getting work, eh? Well, I might have something for you, when you leave Plangomeur. When are you leaving?"

"About Whitsun."

Mademoiselle de Caradeuc stared at her.

"What's the matter? You said that as though it would be a wrench."

"The matter," replied Françoise, "is that, when I leave, people will say, 'She only went there for the money she could get out of it. Now she's got it, and she's going.' Sometimes, to give them the lie, I feel like staying . . . indefinitely."

Aunt Angélique said nothing for a moment or two, while she took in what lay behind Françoise's words. Then she shrugged her shoulders.

"In short, you want to sacrifice yourself for nothing, in order to stop fools saying that you sold yourself. That's it, isn't it? A fine feeling! Well, do you know what they would say? 'She's

106

staying to make sure of inheriting her mother-in-law's money.' That's what they'd say. What age is Lucie? She had your husband when she was thirty-eight. He was a year younger than you, and you're twenty-five. So that makes her sixty-two. Sixty-two! You might hope that you wouldn't have too long to wait. Don't look at me like that! What do you expect people to say? What do you expect them to think? Do you expect them to believe that at the age of twenty-five, and with your looks, you're staying at Plangomeur solely from devotion to the memory of a boy to whom you were married only three months? That's asking the impossible."

"Well then?"

"Well then, listen. A good woman, a little crazier even than myself, has just bequeathed the Society a house, several tons of old books, cases of documents, and an income of ten thousand francs into the bargain. They were all excitement about it at our last meeting. I was afraid some of the weakest of them might have a stroke! With the money, they've decided to engage a secretary-archivist. She'd live in the house, dust the old books, and look after the moths. I'll undertake to get the job for you. There would be a small salary, and that, added to the bit you've got, would enable you to live independently. You don't look the part, but there are certainly some repentant old rakes in the Society who'd be delighted to find a pretty woman among them. They'd never miss a meeting! Besides, your poor father is known in such circles. That's one good thing about our provincial literary societies. No one may know anything about them outside, but among themselves they know everything by heart. Achard du Fraô's daughter means *The History of Political Assassinations*, and she's already one of the family. What do you say to that?"

"It would be very nice."

Old men and old books—what better could Françoise expect, when she was alone in the world and had to earn her own living? But the bitterness of revolt which at once rose up in her made her face taut and her eyes hard. Mademoiselle de Caradeuc, who was watching her, stood up, and came and took her by the shoulders.

"Do you take me for an idiot?" she said. "I only talked about it to see how you'd look. Well, I've seen! . . . Now, are you still capable of answering me a straight question?"

She took Françoise by the chin and lifted it up, as you do with a child when you want to look into his eyes.

"Well, are you?"

"I'll try," Françoise promised.

"Then let's try! . . . Would you consent—later on, of course—to marry again?"

The chin she was holding slipped out of her fingers, because Françoise was shaking her head. Aunt Angélique stepped back.

"No? Why not? From fidelity to the memory of your husband? That poor boy! For fear of what people would say? I've already told you what I think about women who sacrifice their lives to public opinion. They're fools and they're gulls! Because marriage disappointed you? But there are as many marriages as there are husbands. And, with a husband, one can have a child!"

She shouted the word, and Françoise flinched, as though her aunt had touched a sore spot. When she had been driven to despise Luc, she had suddenly transferred her hopes to the child who might be born of him. Let him give her that at least! She had startled him by the fury with which she had rejected the precautions he advised. Even so, her wretched marriage had frustrated her not only in her life as a wife, but also in that life of a mother which she had demanded with all her soul, with all her eager body.

She shrugged her shoulders.

"Quite so. I didn't have one."

"But does that mean that you couldn't have one?" protested Aunt Angélique. "If a man, a real man, asked you tomorrow not to make your life over again, but to make your life with him, and if you liked him, why in Heaven's name should you refuse him? You don't know the answer, eh? You might say no, because you're as obstinate as Manon Brandan's ass, but you couldn't tell him why."

Despite herself, it was to her aunt's tone, rather than her words, that Françoise listened. She recognized it, that loud, nasal voice! She had heard it, eighteen months earlier, singing Luc la Hourie's praises, celebrating the good luck of this unexpected marriage. Then, just as it did today, it had assailed her distrust, her reserve. So her aunt's mania for match-making had taken possession of her again, and, with her old bird's fickleness, she had already forgotten . . . How should Aunt Angélique know that there was no going back on the past, as a little girl does in a game when she says, "That doesn't count," and starting all over again with the same enthusiasm? But Françoise knew.

"You'll find out that I'm right again," her aunt's voice wound up.

At last Françoise smiled, relaxed by her sheer simplicity.

"Are you in a hurry?" asked Mademoiselle de Caradeuc.

"No. Not particularly."

"Then would you do something for me, as you have your car? Do you know Pludual?"

"No."

"All the more reason! He's someone you ought to know.

I've owed him a visit for ages, but he lives miles away from any bus route. It wouldn't be far out of your way, and then you could drop me at Plouër, where I could catch the Dinard bus home."

"All right."

As they set out, Françoise asked, "And how's Serena?"

Aunt Angélique stopped dead and stared at her.

"Still thinking about Serena? She's just a stone that a crazy old woman baptised, for lack of any children to christen. Come on!"

They descended the steep slope to the village, where Françoise had left her car.

As she plumped down in it, Mademoiselle de Caradeuc said, "When I'm dead, put a little child's automobile in my coffin, so that I can take with me something more than regret for not having one."

"Why don't you buy one?"

"Because one must always choose between going away and staying where one is, my dear. If I had one, do you think I'd use it to go shopping in Saint-Servan? Why, I'd spend my life on the road, preferably in Tibet, if there are any roads there. Then who'd do the bit of good there is to be done here? With my income, I can't amuse myself and help others too. I only wish I could."

As they left the village, Françoise had to make a swerve, so sudden that the car's right wing grazed a wall. A boy had rushed out of a farmyard and darted across the road, almost touching the bumper. Aunt Angélique stuck her head out of the window and swore at him.

Then she ordered, "Stop! Stop, will you? I want to box his ears for him."

As she thought about her automatic reaction to save the

boy, Françoise remembered that someone else before her had done the same thing, when he crashed into a plane-tree. She told herself sometimes that she would never have given another thought to Maurière but for his accident, but this scarcely calmed her disturbance.

"Drive slowly, my dear."

It was her sense of appreciation, not fear, that made her aunt speak. For they had arrived just above the Rance, at the entrance to the suspension-bridge, and Mademoiselle de Caradeuc did not want to miss anything during that wonderful crossing: the tawny plain of Mordreuc stretching to the right, its broad belts of blue water, its strips of sand, the ring of fields serving as setting for a sea of pale emerald.

" 'Never did the Nereids drape more exquisite garlands upon the robe of Ceres,' " she quoted. "He certainly knew his Rance. That's why I can forgive him so many exasperating pages in his *Memoires d'outre-tombe*."

Her erudition had seized hold of her again. From la Ville-ès-Nonais onward she stopped bothering about the scenery. Tirelessly, she associated places and antiquities with dates, references and, above all, refutations. For archeology, to her, meant a fight. Lightly she demolished the theories laboriously built up by her colleagues. All the local historians, Elvire de Preissac, Paul Sébillot, Robidou, Abbé Duine recurred in a row in her anathemas. She put nothing in place of their theories, but her relentless fluency laid everything low. Serena herself had strangely changed her shape since she last mentioned her. Now she attributed to her the vile habits of those spirits of death who, so she asserted, were the first sirens. Upon the banks of the Rance she heaped up the bones of victims devoured by Serena. She endowed her with the body of a bird and the head of a woman, like the Coeré hydra in the

Louvre; for she would have nothing to do with those hind-quarters of a fish, which made their appearance only among the jesters of the Augustan age and at fairs. For that matter, she confessed that she would readily have given up believing in Serena at all if many other people had believed in her.

Françoise paid little heed to her aunt. She was on the look-out for any surprises on the winding road. By way of Miniac-Morvan and Plerguer, she had driven up to Roz-Landrieux. The Dol marshes spread out before her, their squares of osier-beds looking lighter than olive-trees.

"Which way now?" she asked.

"Take the Lillemer road," replied her aunt. "It's the second turning on the left."

They drove for five minutes along a white road, on which Françoise slowed down, ashamed of the dust-storm she was raising behind her.

"The drive to the right there," said her aunt. "That's Ploé-zel."

The wooden gate, once white, had almost rotted away. Cart-wheels had rutted the drive, and the tall elms flanking it rose out of a thick tangle of brushwood. At the end, the car stopped in front of an iron gate eaten away by rust. The walls on either side of it had crumbled away, and shoots climbed straight out of the debris.

Mademoiselle de Caradeuc rang the bell. Dogs started barking, and the sound came close. Then slow steps approached. Aunt Angélique made a sign to Françoise, as though to say, "Now, have a good look!"

One side of the gate opened a little, with a creak. It disclosed a face, very pale but very handsome, like that of a Venetian Christ, with a fair beard, short and curly, and brown eyes that stared for a few moments before recognizing the visitors. At length the personage said, "Why, it's you, Mademoiselle! Come in, please!"

He opened the iron gate wider and stood aside.

In the courtyard signs of a neglect still recent were everywhere evident. The flower-beds were outlined; but the yew hedges, no longer trimmed, were burgeoning, and the rose-bushes were disappearing in tall grass, smothered by bindweed. There were broken panes in the windows of the outhouses, and in those of the manor itself. A shutter dangled from one hinge. The two spaniels, their duty done with their welcome, walked back into the house through the wide-open door.

"Comte de Pludual," said Aunt Angélique. "My niece, Madame la Hourie."

Françoise held out her hand. Pludual bent over and brushed it with his lips. His action surprised her, after she had noticed the negligence of his dress, for his gray flannel trousers bagged at the knees, and his white pullover was covered with thick, coarse darns, which stood out like stains. Pludual wore peasant's clogs. When he tried to smile, he disclosed a missing tooth. But what struck Françoise most was his eyelids. They were long and heavy, with a network of blue veins, and he kept them lowered, as though to enclose sleep within them.

He ushered his visitors into a large drawing room. What Françoise noticed first of all was the dust, the same dust as that of the road. It covered everything with an ashen layer, turned the black notes of the piano gray, dulled the gilt of the picture-frames, powdered the marble table-tops. Then there were the flowers, a wealth of big, withered flowers in vases and baskets: skeletons of lilies and irises, marguerites turned into hay, shriveled dahlias in black clusters, roseheads parchment-like at the end of their thorny stalks.

113

Mademoiselle de Caradeuc noticed her niece's surprised look.

"Nothing has been touched here," she explained as soon as she had sat down, "since the death of darling little Cécile, Monsieur de Pludual's sister."

"Nothing has been touched, indeed," Pludual agreed. "But," he added, half-turning toward Françoise, "I sometimes wonder whether it isn't due to laziness on my part even more than respect for the dead."

"How do you mean, laziness?" exclaimed Mademoiselle de Caradeuc.

"Being tired of life," Pludual explained, gently. "The worst kind of laziness . . ."

Even while he was answering her aunt, he kept his eyes fixed on Françoise, an intent stare, with surprise dawning in it. At length he said, "It's strange, but don't you think Madame la Hourie resembles Cécile?"

"Exactly!" cried Mademoiselle de Caradeuc. "I'd never have mentioned it to you, but it struck me the last time I was here. I said to myself, 'Why, that's Françoise!'"

She turned round in her chair, and looked at a pastel in an oval frame on the wall. Françoise looked up at it in turn.

This portrait was the only picture which had been kept dusted. A girl in a rose-colored satin dress looked back at her, with the same insistent gaze with which Pludual was still looking at her. The resemblance which he had just discovered struck Françoise. This was indeed herself, but a more hazy version of her, with more transparency in the coloring, more fragility in the features. But, above all, the expression of the face intrigued Françoise. The portrait gazed at her with quiet mockery. It was barely sketched in its half-smile; but Françoise was as keenly conscious of it as though it were on the lips of a living person. One might have thought that Cécile de Pludual was making fun of this resemblance at which they were marveling. Françoise said to herself, "I could never smile like that." She realized it with a sense of inferiority.

"It's more like a reflection than a resemblance," murmured Mademoiselle de Caradeuc.

"There's another portrait in her bedroom," said Pludual, "in which the likeness is still more striking."

He offered to take them there.

In the bedroom there was the same dust, more noticeable on the delicacy of its silks and trinkets. A summer hat lay fading on a table. A wrap was flung over the arm of a chair. At Plangomeur, Madame la Hourie kept her souvenirs neatly arranged and classified. The housewife prevailed even over the despairing mother. But here life had been allowed to stop at the moment when, for this man, it had lost its savor. Françoise reproached herself for the irritation which this worship of the dead now aroused in her. They were so wretched, all these counterfeits!

Pludual led them to a large photo of Cécile, a head and shoulders in a low-cut evening dress, taken in a Paris studio. His eyes on Françoise, he made his comparison again. But this time Françoise had no hesitation in challenging the likeness. The set features of this enlargement did not belong to her. The face, thus caught in a moment of pose, was stony. Together with the shadows it cast, the flashlight threw into relief a disdainful boredom foreign to Françoise.

Pludual doubtless noticed all this too, for he said, "With this lighting, it looks quite different. Madame la Hourie is—how shall I put it?—better defined, and closer at hand. But just now, in the half-light in the drawing room, the likeness was really striking."

Hurriedly, he opened an album. Every photo in it was one of Cécile, playing tennis, at the seaside, on a picnic, on board ship, playing with dogs in the entrance courtyard, this time kept in order and full of flowers. Every one estranged Françoise from the likeness which had struck her earlier. This was indeed a stranger, someone unknown to her, whose portraits passed before her eyes. The last of them showed Cécile a slim figure in a light dress, standing on the steps of a massive modern building.

"The sanatorium," said Aunt Angélique. "That's where she died."

"Yes, that's where she died," Pludual repeated in a harsh tone, which rang with suddenly reawakened anger. "She wanted so much to come back here to die. She asked to come back. But they wouldn't let her, while there was still time, and then they didn't let me know until it was too late."

Françoise looked at him furtively. His handsome face was drawn.

"They robbed me of her last hours," he muttered.

"But it was so sudden," Mademoiselle de Caradeuc reminded him. "Besides, otherwise you wouldn't have had that lovely consolation she arranged for you."

"That's true," Pludual agreed, suddenly appeased.

"Every week, for months after her death," Aunt Angélique explained, "the Comte received a letter from her. She got a friend, who was to remain unknown, to send them to him. She wrote these letters for after her death. She wrote them to sustain her brother, to console him, above all, to force him to live even without her. Wasn't it wonderful?"

Françoise was in doubt whether it was wonderful or monstrous, this romantic idea of letters from beyond the grave to keep the breath in a living man. Oh, for the heartbroken, but

116

imple sorrow of plain folk! Oh, for their resignation, their calm, their memory that remained faithful, with no need of these deceits, these counterfeit presences which she had just left at Plangomeur and which she found here all over again! How shocking was this dunning of the dead!

Then she reflected that she had no right to judge, since she had never loved her lost one. Still, this visit had become unendurable to her. Pleading the bad roads, she said they must be going.

"But you'll come again, won't you?" said the Comte quickly, as he gazed at her. "It would be a charity as blessed on your part as it would be precious to me."

Mademoiselle de Caradeuc promised that they would come again.

When they reached the gate, Pludual said, "Go by way of the pond and the woods. It's shorter."

It may have been shorter, but the road was riddled with pot-holes, and Aunt Angélique, who had banged her hat against the roof of the car as soon as they set off, swore as she held tight.

When they reached the pond, she ordered, "Stop for a moment!"

She made a point of these stops at various places. Françoise cut off the engine, and the sudden silence struck her. It was as though it made the tall trees cast heavier shadows. They hung far out over the long, narrow pond, and darkened it. The water was bare, without a lily, without a reed. It looked deep and cold. On the other side rocks fell sheer into it.

"Well, what do you think?" asked Aunt Angélique.

Françoise realized that she was asking her opinion not about the pond, but about the man they had just left. She shrugged her shoulders. She really did not know.

117

Her gesture seemed to annoy Aunt Angélique intensely.

"Oh, you can say it without compromising yourself!" she exclaimed. " 'There's a fellow who adored his sister,' eh? So much so that some dirty-minded people—and there are plenty of them about—whispered that he loved her more than a brother should. Oh, yes, that explained everything, of course. She was a shy, sensitive little thing, but, oh, so pretty! Well, you saw her for yourself. And you saw Hervé too. He passed very high out of the Naval College, and then he threw up his career to come and live with his sister when their mother died ten years ago. That's so like us, isn't it? It was senseless, and it was superb. It was thoroughly Breton. He'd have killed himself when she died, without a doubt, but for those letters of hers. He was handed the first when he reached the sanatorium, and the first promised that there would be more. He showed fine courage in going on living after the last of them. But what now? Do you know how it will end? That boy will take to drink."

"Why doesn't he get married?"

Françoise asked the question with indifference, as though she were speaking about some casual acquaintance, because this struck her as the simple, obvious solution. Aunt Angélique seemed taken aback. Then she was delighted that Françoise should have taken the words out of her mouth.

"That's just what I said to him," she cried. "He replied 'To do that would mean finding what I have lost in someone else.' To him that was the end of it; there wasn't another Cécile. But now my friend Hervé meets you, and at first sight your resemblance to her dumbfounds him."

"Oh, no!" Françoise exclaimed. She started her engine again. Then she turned to her aunt, her eyes dark with anger.

"Is that why you took me there?" she demanded.

"Now, listen to me," replied her aunt. "How does just meeting him commit you to anything?"

"No, that's enough!"

Françoise set off furiously along the bumpy side road. The car lurched dangerously.

"You'll kill us!" cried her aunt.

But Françoise did not slow down until she reached the main road. Indignation still kept her hands clenched on the steering-wheel.

So everyone's sole idea about her was to link her up with corpses! She was to become the wife of this other madman. All he would seek in her was the reflection of his dead sister. He would want her to dress like his Cécile, to adopt the attitudes of his Cécile. He would try all the time to force her into that picture-frame. He would demand from her an exact reincarnation of the dead woman, and he would hate her when she refused to lend herself to all this.

She swung the car round corners, cutting them too close, taking them too fast.

"Why, where are you going. Turn to the left!"

It had just dawned on horror-stricken Aunt Angélique that she was being rushed along the Saint-Servan road, exactly in the opposite direction to her way home. But Françoise simply said, curtly, "I have a call to make."

A quarter of an hour later, she stopped her car at the gate of the Saint-Marc Hospital.

"Wait for me five minutes," she said. "I'm going to inquire about a patient."

"Don't forget I have to catch my bus," Aunt Angélique reminded her.

"I'm not going in."

At the porter's lodge Françoise asked her way.

"Monsieur Maurière, please, Sister?"

"He's in the Saint-Jean ward. The second building over there, behind the trees."

There a young nun received her.

"He's much better," she said. "He got up yesterday for the first time."

Then she laughed.

"In fact, he's becoming unbearable, he's so bored. Whom shall I say?"

"You needn't give him my name, Sister. It was some friends of Monsieur Maurière's who asked me to call. They will be very glad to hear that he's better."

Françoise bowed slowly, and went down the steps again.

On the long graveled drive, she passed two workmen. They stared at her intently, and then turned to look after her. By this time Aunt Angélique was drowsing in the warm car. She jumped when Françoise opened the door.

"You haven't been long," she said. "Well, how's the patient?"

"He's better."

"What's the matter with him?"

"He had a car smash."

"Do you know him?"

"He's the engineer who put up the line across our park."

"Oh, yes, I read about it."

They set off again. After a few minutes, Aunt Angélique said, "It's a good thing you went to see him."

"Why?"

"Because now you're driving like a Christian. Force of example, I suppose. It was just the right day for you to visit a man who smashed himself up through speeding."

"He wasn't speeding."

Françoise excused him instinctively. But Aunt Angélique remarked sententiously, "You don't run into a tree unless you're speeding."

A few kilometers farther on, she said, though without seeming to attach any importance to it, "You needn't tell your mother-in-law about our visit. She and Pludual are on bad terms with each other."

She did not say why. But Françoise searched her mind for the reason. When she had found it, she demanded, "Didn't you tell me that Madame la Hourie went to ask for Cécile for Luc?"

Mademoiselle de Caradeuc's lips tightened.

"If I told you that, I'd have done better to keep my mouth shut. Is that what you mean?"

"Oh, no!"

At Plouër, as she got out of the car to wait for her bus, Aunt Angélique asked, "So you really don't like him?"

Françoise shrugged her shoulders again.

"Like that, eh? Well, that's still worse."

Alone on the road again, Françoise's thoughts turned back hastily to that sudden call which she had ventured to make at the hospital. Doubtless Maurière would never know that she had inquired about him; but why had she done it? Was it by way of protest against the role of double for a dead woman which her aunt had tried to impose upon her? Yes, it was! She had fled from the pond, so indignant that she must get her own back, and at once. She had wanted to assert that she was free to do what she liked. For she was free; the absurd visit to that maniac proved it in itself. She thought about the way in which Pludual had stared at her. Then she saw once more the young nun, laughing heartily. "He's becoming unbearable, he's so bored." The wall and the trees of Plangomeur appeared suddenly at a turn, and, late though she was, Françoise slowed down unconsciously, lest she should too soon surrender her freedom of the road, her freedom of thought.

Madame la Hourie was waiting for her on the steps. As soon as she saw the car, she came down, waving. Françoise was surprised at her pallor, and then at the nervous strength with which her mother-in-law gripped her arm, the moment she jumped out of the car.

"I've been dying with anxiety," said Madame la Hourie, very low and very quickly. "Why are you so late? What happened?"

She pulled Françoise toward the house.

"Why, nothing!" replied Françoise. "My aunt had some calls to make. I took her in the car."

Madame la Hourie, who was now going up the steps in front of her, turned round.

"You shouldn't have done it," she retorted. "I imagined at once that something had happened. I thought you'd had an accident."

When they reached the dining room, her head and her hands were shaking. Her anxiety still left her trembling. She sank into an arm-chair. Françoise remained standing. She was astonished. It was the first time her mother-in-law had shown so obviously sincere an emotion about her. Indeed, it made her uneasy. Was her mother-in-law fond of her, after all? Within a few weeks of her going away, must she suddenly strive against this attachment so suddenly revealed? Must she unclasp those fingers which had just imprisoned her own?

Madame la Hourie looked up and gazed at her intently.

"Remember, my dear," she murmured, "if he should come back, after all, it would be I whom he would call to account about you."

As THOUGH he were broken in two,
Grioul suddenly bent over the little
engine which was spluttering between his legs, and cut off the gas,
with an oath. The engine stopped, and the launch drifted
silently. The gardener turned sailor hoisted the red sail and
took the helm.

It was only when he was sitting down that Françoise asked,
in a tone of reproach, "Why do you swear like that?"

Grioul shrugged his shoulders, and smiled slightly out of
the corner of his mouth.

"My brother-in-law is used to it," he replied.

"Your brother-in-law?"

"I have a sister who's a nun at Guingamp. In other words,
she's married to the Good Lord."

He took his pipe out of his mouth and laughed, showing all
his yellow fangs. For, when he set foot in a boat again, even
a toy like this one, he became talkative and facetious once
more. All the same, he apologized for the breakdown of the
engine. During the months that the launch had been laid up,
he had failed to stop thieves forcing the padlock of the crank-
case, stealing the two spark-plugs, and, what was worse, laying hands on the float of the carburetor. He had indeed replaced it with a float made out of a cork soaked in paraffin;
but it was impossible to gauge properly, and Françoise had
seen the result for herself. The float-chamber was flooded, the
gasoline overflowed in all directions, and it might easily set
the launch on fire. Grioul could only hope that at Saint-Servan

he could get one made to fit. For to buy a new one was impossible; the shop had closed down.

"Besides," he added, "until now it would have been no good to talk to Madame about it. She couldn't bear even to hear the word 'boat.' Quite naturally, of course."

Then he warned Françoise, "Mind your head!"

He was about to tack in order to run with the wind dead astern. As the breeze was light, he brought the boat by the lee, checking hard on the sheet and letting the boom swing only very slowly, until the sail bellied fully. Then he made fast to the cleat, knocked out his pipe on the gunwale, and watched his course.

The ebb tide helped them. They glided swiftly past the left bank, close to yellow rocks, below thinly planted thickets. At one point, they passed through a belt of white and rose petals: apple-blossoms snowing down from the top of a steep field. A dory laden with gravel, very low in the water, went by to starboard. Two men were rowing it, keeping well in to the bank to take advantage of the eddy.

Grioul hailed them, "Stick at it!"

The man in the stern contented himself with nodding. They would have sworn at him amicably, but for the presence of the lady sitting beside him.

"You know them?" asked Françoise.

"They're Minquier and his son," replied Grioul.

"Oh, so those are the Minquiers!"

At Plangomeur, as at Rocmarin, the Minquiers meant the enemy. For the past two years the old Communist had gained three or four more votes at every election, a proof that he was influencing the district.

Grioul watched father and son toiling at their oars.

124

"Minquier had a funny visit a week ago," he said. "You've heard about it?"

He looked at Françoise oddly. Françoise supposed that he was talking about another of those cars from Paris, which sometimes stopped at the moss-grown quay beside which the old Red lived. Well-dressed tourists got out; but it was said that they changed in his house, and emerged from it wearing caps, old coats, and red scarves, ready for propaganda work.

"Not this time," said Grioul. "It was someone living here."

He tucked the helm under his arm and sat still, staring at Françoise.

"Why, you must know!" he exclaimed.

"No, I don't," replied Françoise.

"Didn't Madame tell you that she'd been to see Minquier, or why she went there?"

Françoise shook her head.

"Well, it would have been better if she'd talked to you about it," Grioul went on. "She's wasting away, all alone with those ideas of hers. Anyway, she went to Minquier to ask him to write to the Russians in Paris for news about the *Entreprenant.* She even offered him money. We know what Minquier is like, but he wouldn't take anything, and he promised to write at once. You can imagine how flattered he was! Of course, he knew beforehand what the result would be, but he took care not to tell her that. Just imagine it! Madame calling on him, begging him to do something for her—it was quite an occasion for him!"

A fish leaped out of the water close to the boat.

"A mullet," said Grioul. "That's a sign that good weather's setting in. They're catching mackerel off Cézembre. The first of them come into the bay at the same time as the first swallows."

But Françoise was not listening to him. She was absorbed in her astonishment. So her mother-in-law had got someone to write to the Soviet Embassy, just a few days after Captain Gennebault's visit. And it was to Minquier that she had gone to beg him to do this for her. Madame la Hourie subscribed liberally to election-committees of the Right. She mobilized her farmers; she lent her car to drive cripples to the poll. And now she had got to the point of using Minquier as an intermediary to ingratiate herself with the Soviet Government!

"How do you know?" Françoise asked.

Grioul shrugged a shoulder.

"They brag about it to anyone who's ready to listen to them, as you may imagine."

"But Madame hasn't said anything to you?"

Grioul took his pipe out of the corner of his mouth.

"Well, she's only talked to me about it while pretending to talk about something else. She's come to me a dozen times in the greenhouse to ask me about Newfoundland, about my trawling there, about being adrift, about wrecks, about people escaping from them. We fishermen are all talkative. We love telling about what we've endured on the Banks. We pile on the agony rather than the other way round. But I saw at once what she was after, and I didn't say a word to her to deceive her. It would have been a sin."

"To deceive her? How do you mean?"

"Why, by leading her to believe that anyone could have been saved from the *Entreprenant!* That's what she wanted to make me say, don't you see? She asked me: 'Have you ever known anyone get ashore in a boat?' She said: 'People are

126

often saved on wreckage, aren't they, when a ship goes down close to the coast?' I've known some who were, of course, fellows as strong as lions who held out for days, clinging to a plank or a barrel, until they were picked up. But I wasn't going to tell her that."

Grioul winked, and stared at Françoise with what she took to be a kind of complicity.

"You were quite right," she said.

"It's just the same about this boat," Grioul went on. "She'd never let me even mention it. Yet it was she herself, the day before yesterday, who came and asked me whether it was in working order. It was your husband who got it built, at Carantec. It's too light for my fancy. I'd have liked to have it a good fifteen feet, with five hundred pounds of ballast at the bottom. But of course the chick always knows better than the hen. To return to Madame, why has she suddenly started to concern herself about the boat, when she'd told me to let it rot? She even came to have a look at it, the day when I was repainting the name."

The boat's name, *Luciole,* had set Françoise's teeth on edge the first time she had seen it, for its owner had had the first three letters, *Luc,* painted bigger and thicker than the others.

She shook her head.

"All this doesn't prove much."

Grioul gazed into the distance.

"That's a matter of opinion. For my part, I say that when she stooped to call on the Minquiers, she must have had some idea at the back of her head."

They were on the point of landing. Grioul shortened sail off the wind and came alongside. The trefoiled tower of Solidor disappeared behind the sail.

Françoise jumped onto the jetty, to which Grioul was holding on with his stubby hands to keep the boat against the stonework.

"As you're leaving the boat at the engineers'," she said, "perhaps I'll meet you at the five o'clock bus."

Grioul shook his head.

"I shouldn't think so. I've a lot to do in connection with the garden. I've got to get some panes of glass cut for the forcing-frames, and I've got to pick up some carnations. I can't count on catching anything before the last bus."

That meant that he was going to take his time, and come back completely drunk. But this was a matter of course whenever he went to town, unless he had to drive the car himself.

Once on the quay, Françoise hurried away, for she had only time to do her shopping before the bus left.

On the way back, as the bus lurched through the flat country-side, she reflected about what Grioul had told her. So, when her mother-in-law bent over her coarse knitting, her knitting for the poor, done with drab wool and intended for warmth and nothing else, she was really, in imagination, setting out for the Arctic, searching its coasts. But what was she looking for there? A living man? Not at all. That was Grioul's explanation, a bit of romantic fiction. For her part, Françoise supposed that Luc's mother had found a fresh way in which to pursue her son. During all these past months, had she not followed him up through every phase of his childhood and his youth? Had she not harried him even through his twelve weeks as a married man? Now she felt strong enough to seize upon his last hours. His shipwreck lured her. She would prowl around it, trembling, tortured, but greedy. It was going to be heartbreaking, and it was going to be nasty.

128

She was still thinking about this when she turned into the drive at Plangomeur. Suddenly she heard branches being brushed aside in the undergrowth, to her right, and Maurière jumped down into the ditch. He was thin and pale. But he still had that mocking air which she loathed. At the sight of her surprise, it bore witness to the success of his ambush.

"So," he said, as he stepped up on to the drive, "I'm reduced to lying in wait for you in the woods. And you can't even blame me, since you refuse to receive me. You're walking very fast. Are you afraid of me?"

"No!"

He had found the one question capable of stopping her dead, in the middle of the drive. That made him laugh loudly: that laugh of his which showed off his fine teeth only too well.

"Good!" he exclaimed. "In any case, I won't keep you long. There are just one or two things that I don't understand, and I'd like you to explain them to me. Six weeks ago, you sent me word, through one of my workmen, that things had gone far enough and you were turning me the cold shoulder. You gave him the message at the very moment when I was ringing at your door. It was a fine trick, and I fell for it. But not without saying a word. The silent role doesn't suit me. I lost my temper properly with my workmen. Then I packed up and cleared out. I got it, all right! The next thing was that I ran into my plane-tree; and you telephoned to the hospital to find out whether I was well and truly killed. I won't tell you whether it was the receptionist or the probationer who told me. Why did you telephone? A twinge of remorse? Maybe. Or was it that you inquired about me because I worked for you, just as one does in the case of old servants? But then, three weeks later, you came in person to Saint-Servan to ask about me. Two of my workmen recognized you. That, perhaps, I don't understand quite so well. The one thing certain is that I owe you my thanks. . . ."

"No, you don't!"

Françoise said it so violently that, despite his determination to be mocking, he was taken aback for a moment. Then his eyes darkened. He broke off a branch as he walked along, and switched the tree-trunks with it.

"In any case," he went on, "that gives me a right to talk to you for five minutes. After all, I've a visit to repay you, and I've something to say to you. As I don't know how to dress things up or trick them out, I'll serve it out to you plain, without any sugar, just as I think it. I've always said that I'd never marry, that I was going to stay free. Since I met you, I haven't said so much about it. Of course, if there were even the tiniest hope, I'd wait as long as necessary. But there isn't any hope, is there? It's 'No,' eh?"

"It's 'No.' "

"But why? You know, I'm not in the habit of proposing marriage at every turn. I can assure you that you're the first. It's nothing to laugh about. That shows that you don't understand at all. It's a serious matter, I've said it seriously, and you can listen to it seriously."

"I've answered you seriously."

"Very good. But there remains the 'why.' One can always refuse, but one owes a reason, or at least a pretext. So?"

"I've no wish to marry again."

Maurière shrugged his shoulders.

"You were married for three months. Is that any reason for living alone for the rest of your life? You're not that kind of girl."

He stared at her boldly, his head lowered a little, his eyes

130

looking up. Françoise stared back at him tensely. Her stubborn voice barely parted her lips, set hard, as she replied, "You're wrong. I am that kind of girl."

Maurière's voice rang shamelessly in the wood.

"Oh, no, you're not! I'm not wrong. There's nothing about you of those widows who grow fat and take themselves off on Sundays, with a brush and a watering-can, to attend to their husbands' graves. Tell me that you don't like me. Tell me that you'll only accept a man of your own class. That may be true. But don't tell me that you'll always refuse to marry again! Oh, no! You may not know it, but you're waiting for someone."

Drawn up to her full height, almost as tall as Maurière, her gray eyes fixed on his dark eyes, Françoise flung at him, "Not you, in any case!"

"Are you sure of that?"

He turned around and seized her by the arms, above the elbows, in a hard grip. At first it was as though he wanted only to keep her still while he stared at her. Then his taut arms flexed to draw her toward him, to bring her right up against him. Bending back, she resisted, her teeth clenched, without a word, but she did not take her eyes off his. It was only when she gave way, vanquished, only when her breast touched his own, that she turned her head away.

"You're a brute!" she said, in a very low voice.

"I am," he agreed, in the same breathless tone.

He pressed her against him.

"I'll shout for help," she warned him.

"No, you won't! Oh, no, you won't!"

He had felt her muscles relax, an almost imperceptible consent on the part of her body.

It was at this moment that he leaned against her. His em-

131

brace did not loosen, but it turned into a clutching hold, which kept on weakening. Suddenly he gave way at the knees. Françoise held him up.

"What's the matter?" she asked.

Deathly pale to his very lips, beads of sweat on his brow, Maurière staggered back toward a beech. Leaning against its trunk, his eyes closed, he summoned up all his strength not to collapse before Françoise's eyes.

"Lie down!" she advised him.

Maurière shook his head.

"You must lie down," Françoise persisted.

He slid down the trunk, and lay on the moss.

"Go away!" he stammered. "Leave me alone! Go away!"

"No, I won't!"

This time, Françoise spoke more gently. Then she ran to the stream, soaked her handkerchief, and wiped his face with it. After a few moments, a little color came back into his cheeks.

"I hurt my head in the accident," he muttered. "It's not right yet."

Then he closed his eyes. When he opened them again, he saw Françoise kneeling beside him.

"Why don't you go away?" he repeated.

This time, Françoise did not answer.

With difficulty, Maurière put his hands behind him, and propped himself on his palms to help himself up.

"I'm all right now," he said.

"No, you're not," replied Françoise. "Rest a little longer."

When he was on his feet, still unsteady, she asked, "Will you come to the house?"

It was, she remembered, just what she had said to Luc when

he came out of the water. He had accepted at once, but Maurière refused.

"No, thanks. My car's only three hundred yards away."

He took two or three steps, still staggering.

"Take my arm," Françoise suggested.

He took it, and leaned on it. Then he shook his head.

"Making such a fool of myself! . . ."

He clenched his teeth with rage as he spoke. To take his mind off his humiliation, Françoise asked, "How did it happen, that accident of yours?"

He replied in an exasperated tone, "It was either the tree or the little girl. I chose the tree."

He let go of Françoise's arm.

"I can manage now."

He walked on, his head down, his face drawn with the anger which had come back to him with his strength.

"That amused you, didn't it?" he asked. "You don't show it too much. You're still too kind-hearted."

Françoise shrugged her shoulders.

"Oh, yes," Maurière went on, "women love to see a man brought low. I'm more interesting now than I was before. But this won't last, I warn you. I just want time to make good the blood I lost. I bled like a stuck pig. It's only a question of feeding up. I'd rather blow my brains out than go on being the rag-doll you picked up just now."

His words struck Françoise again with all the rough strength that he invoked. She remembered how La Hourie, the corsair, wounded with a broken knee-cap, had ended his assault on Tortosa astride the shoulders of one of his men. She thought better of Maurière because he despised himself for having let go. She could see his strength coming back to him like a flood. It was shown by the renewed swing of his stride, by the rhythm of marching in his broad shoulders, which were beginning to work again as they should. She recalled the hardness of his hands when they seized her. It must have left its mark on her arms. The thought made her blush. Was it from embarrassment or a kind of pleasure?

Maurière was walking faster now, as though he were in haste to be done with it. The wood ended at the roadside in a sheer drop. Maurière jumped, but deliberately he did so into the ditch, ankle-deep in mud. Then he turned round to help Françoise. When she saw his hands stretched out, ready to clasp her again, she stepped aside, jumped in her turn, and landed firmly on the other side of the ditch.

They walked on to the turn in the road where Maurière had left his car. As they reached it, the clatter of clogs came nearer, and Annette made her appearance, walking with her wiry step. She looked up at the couple coming toward her. When she recognized them, her surprise was made manifest by her sudden slowing down, by the steady stare of her wide-open eyes. Then she pulled herself together, lowered her eyes and went past them, tight-lipped, without seeming to see them.

"That's your cook, isn't it?" said Maurière. "She'll go and tell everyone that she's seen us walking together. Now you're nicely compromised!"

Françoise shrugged her shoulders. No, Annette wouldn't say anything, or, at least, only when it suited her.

When they reached the car, Maurière looked at Françoise.

"Now's the time for me to thank you. But I'm so bad at it I'd sooner hold my tongue. Thanks, all the same."

He turned the handle of the door slowly.

"So it's 'No,' eh? Now, wait a minute! Don't say anything! After all, there's one thing you could do, without losing your reputation. You could put off your 'No' for a fortnight. You could look as though you were thinking it over. That would be more flattering to me, wouldn't it? Listen: I'm going away for ten days to Savoy, to see my mother. She thought I was killed, poor dear, and she won't be really sure I'm not until she has a chance to kiss me. When I get back, I'll come and ask you whether you haven't changed your mind. Meanwhile, I don't want to hear anything about it."

He opened the door, stooped to get into the car, slammed the door, waved his hand curtly, and drove off so fast that Françoise stood still for a few moments on the road, quite taken aback.

On her way back to Plangomeur, she remembered that Annette had seen her. So much the better! She had made up her mind not to handle things with kid gloves any longer. In that wood a hard game had been played in which her victory had been narrowly won. Desire had enveloped her, pervaded her, and it had freed her. Maurière had thrust her boldly toward life. He had shouted at her that she would never stay in the service of shadows. If he had known about them, he would have cursed the old gentlemen, the old manuscripts, that Aunt Angélique held in reserve for her. "You're waiting for someone." Those insolent words of his had made her indignant. But she repeated them as she went back to Plangomeur, almost as though they were a promise.

The next day but one, Françoise received a letter.

It bore the heading of the district attorney at Saint-Servan. It informed her that, after administrative inquiry, the court, by collective judgment, had declared the death of all the members of the *Entreprenant's* crew to be established. Her husband, however, as he did not appear on the roll-call of the crew and had embarked in the capacity of a passenger, was not included in the judgment. In order to obtain judicial declaration of his death, it devolved upon his widow to take steps as soon as possible in accordance with articles 855 *et seq.* of the Code of Civil Procedure. Her request should be addressed to the Minister of Marine, at the suite of the Public Prosecutor.

Françoise refolded the letter. It arrived with the aptness of a reply. She herself had never made any official inquiry; but she had heard, through the wives of some of the lost men, that there had been an administrative investigation. She knew, too, that Luc's position aboard the trawler had excluded him from this task of common burial. And now here she was called upon to free herself, like the other wives, in the eyes of the law.

She had always despised the laziness of those devout people who made use of Providence as though it were a kind of upper servant, imposed tasks upon it for a given date, required replies from it as though they were working an oracle, and demand that it should upset the course of the world for the sake of the smallest of their private interests. But she believed, because a Christian woman should believe, in things wrought in life by the hand of God. This letter was an act of Providence.

In search of Madame la Hourie, Françoise went up to her bedroom. Inside she could hear an animated conversation. The voices stopped the moment she knocked at the door. Her mother-in-law was sitting in an arm-chair near the window. Annette, her back turned, was pretending to run through her account-book. Françoise felt that they had just formed an alliance against her. She held out the sheet of paper.

"I've just received this letter."

Madame la Hourie read it at arms' length, without putting on her glasses.

"Well?" she demanded.

136

She looked her daughter-in-law straight in the eyes, as though combat were offered her sooner than she expected, and she accepted it.

Françoise refolded the letter.

"I'm going to apply for judicial declaration," she replied.

Her mother-in-law sank her head, but it was too low for dejection. She was obviously assembling all her resources of anger and indignation.

When she raised her face, her mouth was drawn by a grimace of contemptuous hatred which curled back her upper lip and lengthened her heavy chin. Her shoulders and arms twitched as though she had an itch. Her trunk moved, her slippers pawed the floor, her fingers feverishly crumbled emptiness, as though she were trying to get up. All these movements went together with a peculiar tremor of her body, stuck in the arm-chair and seeking to drag itself away from it.

"Ugh!" she growled, in a tight-lipped sneer which ended in a grunt of fury. "So he's not dead enough for you? He's in your way. You're going to ask them to guarantee that he's dead, in black and white. A missing man may still come back. A dead man's surer."

"I've waited longer than I need," retorted Françoise. "All the others . . ."

"All the others needed money," Madame la Hourie interrupted. "It was to get their insurance that they wanted the deaths declared. But you—you haven't the excuse that you're waiting for money."

Françoise drew herself up.

"No, indeed," she said. "If I needed an excuse, certainly I haven't got that one."

By this time her mother-in-law had slid forward to the extreme edge of her chair, as though on the point of hurling herself out of it. Without even listening to Françoise's reply, she went on volubly, "You're afraid, you're afraid that he'll come back. Yesterday you were praying for him as though he were dead. Today you want it written down that he's dead, that he won't come back to claim you."

Françoise's calm had once worn down the blustering wrath of Achard du Fraô. It was in the even voice of those days that she repeated: "I'm going to apply for judicial declaration. After all, it'll only a formality. My husband has been dead for a year, and . . ."

Brandishing her short arms, her fists clenched, Madame la Hourie cried, "That a bad wife wants him dead doesn't make him dead. No, that doesn't make him dead. No, no, no!"

The word rose to the shrill tone where her voice usually broke. This time it did not break. When Françoise, deliberately turning her back on her, left the room, those cries of "No!" still reached her through the heavy door she had closed behind her.

138

THE man still stood in the middle of the room, but he was more at ease now. He gesticulated as he said, "It was when the pumps gave out and the ship was sinking under our feet that I seized hold of a piece of grating, and then I found myself in the sea with it."

CHAPTER EIGHT

"In a shipwreck," Madame la Hourie asked, "there's often flotsam like that to which one can cling, isn't there?"

"Why, always, Madame, always! As you can imagine, when a cyclone hits you, everything on deck is blown off. Hatch-covers and barrels are carried away. In a trawler, there are the partition-planks, too."

"The *Entreprenant* carried two rafts."

"Quite so. And rafts always float, wrong side up as well as right side. They'll carry a score of men each, even when the boats are smashed to matchwood. Well, I lashed myself to my grating, for fear of being washed off it, and I was on it when the whaler picked me up two days later."

"Not till two days later?"

"Yes, two days. That's what they told me when I came to life again, for I was half-dead with cold and exhaustion. They were on their way to fish in the Bering Straits. There was no question of their putting back for my sake. Besides, they were a man short, and there were some husky fellows aboard to reckon with. So there was nothing to do but make the best of it and work at that killing job of theirs for two years."

"Two years!"

"Yes, Madame, two whole years. And, at the end of them,

a dollar and your gun! When accounts are made up, the captain always swears that he hasn't made a cent of profit. So he can't pay you, but he makes you a present of your gun. Though it seems about the last present to make to a man you don't pay! To take it and say 'Thank you' as well, you have to be well trained. But they train you, all right!"

"And then you came back to France?"

"Oh, not at once, Madame. First of all I had to find a consul. You see, they're more than half pirates aboard those ships, and they're not very fond of big ports. They go in for smuggling as well as whaling. Besides, with one dollar you can't go very far or very fast. It was not until five months after they'd landed me that I found a captain at Dakoma who was ready to give me a passage home."

"And when you got home, no one expected you any more?"

"No one. What do you think? After two years and a half!"

"Everyone thought you were dead?"

"I should say so! When I walked without warning into the *Rendez-vous de la Marine*, a little bar in Blainville in La Manche—that's where I come from—they thought I was the devil himself. The landlady dropped her salad-bowl."

The old sailor laughed, a low, open-mouthed laugh that showed the gaps in his teeth. His name was Charlot, but everyone knew him by his nickname. "Proof Spirit," given him because of the quantity of brandy he consumed. He was said to drink a hogshead a year. He had a ruddy complexion and white hair. He wore a queer kind of dressing-gown in brown and black check, a gift from an English traveler, and laced sandals on his bare feet. He wandered about the beaches, teaching swimming in the summer, and fishing for conger-eel and crabs in the autumn. In the winter, he drank his pension and the gifts which, shrewd scrounger that he was, he gleaned in the

chateau and middle-class houses. Madame la Hourie had hastened to his hovel as soon as she heard about his having been
shipwrecked. Now he was standing in her room talking, a thin
thread of crafty watch on her showing between his half-closed
eyelids.

"Suppose your son were cast away somewhere on the coast
of Lapland. The currents carry you ashore thereabouts.
Friends of mine who've fished in the White Sea have told me
so. Suppose he were picked up by a seal-fisher. Those waters
are full of them in the summer. You mustn't think that he
could get back from there when he liked. Oh, no! He'd have
to spend the whole season with them. And when the fishing isn't
good, the sealers winter in a bay and start again the next year.
In a case like that, there'd be plenty of delay, you know."

Madame la Hourie listened to him with dreadful eagerness,
huddled in her arm-chair, but with her head raised and her eyes
fixed on the sailor's ruddy face.

"I never thought of those sealers," she said, in a voice
choked by renewed hope.

Proof Spirit made a gesture which invoked the obvious.

"But that's just the kind of thing that happens. They have to
visit all the bays, you see, not only for their fishing, but also to
prepare the oil. If they find a castaway, they pick him up, of
course. But that's no reason why they should make port before
they've got their catch. And that takes months. Besides, they're
tucked away at the back of nowhere, those ports in the north of
Norway or in Siberia. It takes time to get back from them."

Madame la Hourie turned round, for someone was knocking at the door.

"Come in!" she cried, impatiently.

Françoise made her appearance. From the threshold she
could see that the two of them were embarrassed. Proof Spirit

141

glanced at her suspiciously, and then stared at his feet with a fatherly air. Her mother-in-law's eyelids fluttered, and her smile was constrained.

"Grioul wants to know if you're going out today," said Françoise. "Otherwise he'll go and fetch some oil himself. The barrel's nearly empty."

"But of course I'm going out," replied her mother-in-law. "It's Wednesday!"

Every Wednesday, Madame la Hourie paid a visit to one of her farms; she owned farms as far away as Lannion. She came back tired, but excited after inspecting crops and counting beasts and bundles of firewood.

"All right. I'll tell him."

Françoise went out again. She knew just what that vagabond was doing there, and she despised him for raising, for the sake of a few sous, false hopes for which that old woman would have to pay in fresh disappointment. She despised him, but she was not afraid of him. Such fancies were no concern of hers.

For her part, she had other questions to decide. She was fighting passionately within herself for or against Maurière. Sometimes she sided violently with him against herself as the daughter of the Fraôs who proclaimed his vulgar insolence, against herself as the sister of Hélène—Hélène who had punished herself with death for yielding to just such boorish advances as he had dared to make. At such times, she called his effrontery frankness, and his brutality decisiveness. Then, suddenly, she refused to lie to herself. It was a matter merely of physical attraction. Let her accept the fact. His sunburned face, his incisive laugh, the strength of his hot hands, the firmness of his chest when he had pressed her against him . . . But was it not permissible to yield to all this? Was it not possible to find happiness in it?

Then Françoise recalled the harsh words of a Lenten preacher, one of those Breton Franciscans who called themselves "the heavy cavalry of the Church." "If you feed only the flesh, the spirit and the heart die of hunger, for they are not nurtured by flesh." That was why Hélène had killed herself. She had come to see that it would always be forbidden to Hélène du Fraô to find satisfaction in the arms of a boor.

It was about Hélène that Françoise was thinking as she entered the dining room. The anniversary of her death was approaching. She must have a Mass said for her.

"I'm going to keep Charlot at Plangomeur," her mother-in-law announced. "He can help Grioul. He'll have his meals in the kitchen, but he'll go home for the night."

Madame la Hourie sat down, and, as she did before every meal, shifted her plate and her glasses in exact little moves, like draughts on a board.

"It will be an act of charity," she went on. "He could still fish a little last summer, and he gave some swimming-lessons; but now his rheumatism won't let him get into the water."

She hesitated for a moment, and then, watching Françoise, she said: "He was saying to me that survivors from the *Entreprenant* may have been rescued by a seal-fisher."

"They would have had to get ashore first," replied Françoise.

"But that's not impossible either. They went down quite close to the coast. Captain Gennebault told us so. In that case . . ."

"The Sisters of Charity," Annette announced. There were two of them, and they stopped together at the door of the big room. Madame la Hourie stood up.

"Come in, Sisters. We were expecting you."

They were Gray Sisters, who came round every year in the spring, collecting alms in the parish. Madame la Hourie always kept them for lunch. One of them was young, with rosy cheeks and limpid, very alert eyes, which she had not yet learned to control. The other, who was old, and at once decisive and restrained, spoke for the two of them, watching the effect of her words in her hearer's expression. Before dessert, Madame la Hourie asked them for the prayers of their community.

"It's for the safety of a shipwrecked man, Sister. A ship in which my son was sailing was lost last year. But we have heard since that she was lost quite close to a coast, and that he may have got ashore. It's only a tiny hope as yet, but, if God wills, He may restore him to us. I wouldn't refuse you anything . . ."

"We shall ask our Sisters and our orphans for their prayers, Madame."

Françoise looked up in alarm. So this idea of Luc's rescue, this dream with which her mother-in-law whiled away the hours, had become a hope which she avowed publicly! With what nicety had she combined resignation, doubt, expectation!

The young nun stopped peeling her apple. With the dauntless optimism of her youth, with her quiet faith in the miraculous, she said, "When we come back next year, Madame, perhaps we shall find all of you reunited."

She folded her red hands on the edge of the table. Madame la Hourie clasped them in her own. It was in a breathless voice, that obsessed, suddenly pining voice of hers, that she exclaimed:

"Thank you, Sister, thank you! I can't tell you how much good you've done me."

Early in the afternoon the two nuns set off in the car with Madame la Hourie, who had offered them a lift to the next village.

About three o'clock, Annette made her appearance in the study, where Françoise was writing.

144

"Monsieur de Pludual is here," she said, in her offhand tone. "He's asking to see you."

Françoise was surprised. It was the duty of the housemaids to announce visitors. It must be a very unexpected visitor when the old housekeeper took the trouble to do so. When Françoise told her to show Monsieur de Pludual in, Annette seemed to hesitate, then she shrugged her shoulders, and went out.

Françoise found her visitor standing at one of the drawing-room windows, looking out at the park. The moment he turned round as she entered, she could tell that he was scrutinizing her intently and comparing her with the image that haunted him. But this lasted only for a moment. Then Pludual smiled.

"I'm afraid I've got in rather under false pretenses," he said, apologetically. "I knew your mother-in-law wouldn't be here. It's her day for . . . inspection, and, as she doesn't like meeting me . . . I wanted to talk to you in the first place about one of my farmers who's going to become one of yours."

While he recommended the farmer, Françoise studied in surprise his well-cut suit, his neatly knotted tie, his fine shirt. She had imagined him devoted to the darned clothes he had worn at Ploézel. All she could recognize was his face. But he looked even more fragile than at the time of their first meeting. His dark eyelids were heavier than ever, and his cheekbones stood out feverishly.

In his warm, rather drawling voice, he said, "Besides, I didn't want to go on regretting having thanked you so poorly for your visit to me. It did me so much good."

Françoise was annoyed. She brushed the remark aside. "So much good!" He was saying just what her mother-in-law had said to the nun. Already, at Ploézel, she had noticed a re-

145

semblance in their inconsolable attitudes, and she did not like it.

"So few people understand that one can live with a memory, for a memory," Pludual went on. "I felt at once that you understood it. Then there was that strange likeness which took me aback. I've often reproached myself since for showing that too clearly."

After a pause, he added, in a lower tone, "For you ought to be welcomed . . . and admired for yourself."

Françoise shook her head. His ingratiating compliments irritated her.

Hervé de Pludual promptly returned to the subject of the farmer. He recommended him in a few well-chosen words: a large family; the father a hard worker, but touchy; the mother ill and working herself to death. During her lifetime, his sister Cécile had looked after her and brought her medicine. He had continued to do so. He had also interested himself in one of the younger sons, a boy of twelve, remarkably intelligent, with the makings of a good scholar. Pludual was sorry that he could not go on following his career.

"I'm very fond of children," he said, "and they must know it, for they've never been frightened of me, even at my worst moments. In any case, I couldn't help being interested in this boy. He's such a sensitive, eager little creature. If you'll kindly keep an eye on him, you won't regret it, and I shall be most grateful to you."

Françoise promised that she would.

There was a moment's silence. Françoise could see that Pludual was hesitating on the brink of a question. At length he made up his mind to ask it.

"I've heard that you've had news about the wreck, that you've learned some details. Is that true?"

146

Françoise felt now that he was studying her for her own sake. To his consideration of her he brought that shrewdness of solitary men whose attention is not frittered away on trifles. She felt, too, without quite knowing why, that her reply meant much to him. So she told him what had happened at Plango-meur since Gennebault's visit: Madame la Hourie's approach to the Soviet embassy; Charlot's delusion of her with false promises; the hope which she was now pinning on the sealers. Pludual sat still as he listened.

"Do you know how your mother-in-law presents the case?" he asked. She simply says, 'The Russian authorities have ordered the coast to be searched for survivors.' That has set tongues wagging, of course—so much so that I took the liberty of coming to see you. I simply had to know what you thought."

He gazed at Françoise in a peculiarly penetrating way, and went on, "The awful thing about deaths at sea is the sudden silence, the abrupt gap. On land, death is something you can see, something with which you come in contact. At sea, no one sees anything, or hears anything, or knows anything. A radio stops working, and that's all. So one can imagine anything, one can believe anything. The proof of all this is that, after more than a year, your mother-in-law has started waiting again. It's terrible for her. But what about you?"

"About me?"

"Yes. It's quite natural that a mother should be unreasonable where her son is concerned. But you—you don't believe it's possible that he'll come back?"

"After sixteen months? It's out of the question."

"Of course it is," Pludual agreed. "Still, take care! Hope is contagious. It depends on so many things—even on the weather."

Hope? Françoise shook her head, bitterly.

"No!" she exclaimed.

Pludual realized that she had no hope, that all she could have was fear. He nodded agreement again.

Then, playing with his gloves, he said, "Except for my respectful sympathy, I've no right to give you advice. But I'll take the liberty of putting you on your guard. Don't let yourself be sacrificed to an illusion, however touching it may be. Death is not a kind of promotion. It doesn't confer any right on a person who is gone, if he hadn't got it beforehand."

Françoise was astonished to hear him say this. Coming from his lips, it was almost apostasy. He said nothing more for a few moments. Then his face cleared, and his slight smile seemed to mock at what he went on to say.

"It's quite absurd, but when I think about you, it's rather as though you were besieged. I feel as though I were coming to your aid, running a blockade, encouraging your defense. I cast myself only for the most flattering of roles, you see."

He stood up.

"I'm sure I've been very indiscreet, but it is the privilege of those who have suffered to foresee dangers and warn their friends against them."

He looked at Françoise gravely.

"Yes, I'm afraid there's danger."

With a sweep of his hand, he brushed away any possible misunderstanding.

"I fear it *for you*, that goes without saying."

The carelessness with which he abandoned Madame la Hourie to these dangers amused Françoise. He walked toward the door. Then he turned round.

"You don't believe me? So much the better, perhaps."

But, when he reached the door, looking down, he murmured, as though to himself, "I think there are times when one can

148

take back one's life from a dead person only by giving it to a living person."

"So Pludual has been here?" Madame la Hourie demanded, hastening into the room, breathless and red in the face.

"Yes," replied Françoise.

"He dared to come here again! He knew very well that I wasn't here. It's Wednesday. He remembered that I'm out every Wednesday. So he came to see you. Did you know him?"

"I went to Ploézel with my aunt one afternoon."

"You never told me that. If you had, I should have warned you. I won't have him here. Annette knows that very well, but she says he insisted on seeing you. And you told her to show him in."

"I had no reason for refusing to see him."

"If you'd told me about your visit to him, I would have given you some reasons."

From her mother-in-law's excitement, Françoise realized that she could not keep silent on the subject any longer. So she waited. Madame la Hourie brought up a chair and plumped down beside her.

"Listen, my dear Françoise. I can tell you all about it now. When I wanted to get Luc married, I thought about the Pludual girl. He rather liked her. I went to see her brother. I talked to him about it. He told me that he'd think it over, that Cécile was very young—she was just a year younger than Luc!—that he'd consult her. I came away quite satisfied. Luc went to Ploézel sometimes to play tennis. Pludual let him go. Then one day, in a wood—in a wood, I tell you, just like a footpad—he made a frightful scene with Luc. He threatened him. He dared to tell him that he wasn't going to let his sister marry some- one . . ."

149

She stopped dead, her eyes dilated, as though on the very brink of a precipice which she had suddenly realized was there. It was Françoise who finished the sentence for her.

"Someone who had come out of a madhouse."

"So you knew about that?"

"Yes."

Madame la Hourie was taken aback only for a moment. To Françoise's astonishment, she went on, shamelessly, "A 'fugitive from a madhouse'—that's what he said, that's what he dared to say! It left the poor boy still trembling hours afterward. A shameful scene! Just like a footpad! . . . But it was the same kind of thing whenever there was any question of his sister's marriage. That set people talking. They were bound to talk. You can guess what they were likely to say."

"Yes, and I think it's scandalous!"

Madame la Hourie smiled sarcastically.

"Really? Some people could tell you a lot about it. . . . But she's dead. Let's leave that alone. . . . To get back to what I was saying, Pludual didn't content himself with his attack on Luc. There were other girls among our friends whom he—in short, whom he might have thought about. Pludual set all their parents against him. I know he did."

"There was one whom he didn't warn."

"Who?"

"Myself."

"Don't worry about that. If Pludual had known you . . ."

Françoise stared at her mother-in-law. She had spoken quite naturally, without shame, without beating about the bush. She was quite incapable, as she always was when passion got the better of her, of choosing what to say or what not to say. She was so little conscious of the savage simplicity of her reply that Françoise felt ashamed for her.

150

To change the conversation, she asked, "Do you think the curate would give Latin lessons to the elder of the little Bertins? He seems to be an intelligent boy."

As a rule, when Madame la Hourie was thus turned aside in her conversation, she stopped, disconcerted. Then, at Françoise's firm insistence, she changed over slowly, and at first with an effort, to the new subject. But this time she dodged.

"Perhaps," she replied. "We can ask him. . . . But I was talking to you about that—that nursing-home. I'm so glad that I can talk to you about it now! I'll tell you all about it: why he went there and how he lived there. That photograph I gave you for your room, the one I had enlarged by Barthé, was taken at Aurillac when I went to inquire about him. I didn't want to tell you that. But now I shall be able to tell you all I suffered during those ten months. He was lost to me, just as he is today. But he came back. So that martyrdom of three years ago—if you only knew how I bless it! Today, just as I was three years ago, I'm sure that he'll come back. You'll see I shall be right just as I was right three years ago. I'm not mistaken. I can't be mistaken. I've been through it all before."

She flung her head back.

"I'm as sure that he's alive as I was when I felt him stir in my womb."

She said it with such faith that Françoise was impressed.

That evening, at dinner, Françoise found a letter with no envelope beneath her napkin. To her astonishment, she recognised Luc's handwriting. But it was a trembling, jerky handwriting, with its letters uneven and a wealth of capitals. Above all, there was a signature adorned with flourishes, embellished with embroideries, which contrasted absurdly with the breathless text.

"I'll come back, dearest Mother. I am far, far away, but

I'll come back. I'll come back, I swear it. Soon, quite soon. Nothing can stop La Hourie coming back. Look out for me. I shall soon be kissing you."

"You'd swear he'd just written it, wouldn't you?" demanded Madame la Hourie. "He wrote it after I'd left him there."

"Oh, I see!"

Françoise laid the letter slowly on the tablecloth. Despite its frantic scrawl, and although she knew it had been sent from the asylum, this letter seemed to her to come from that mysterious region where her husband had disappeared. From its very first words she had been forcibly struck by its ring of the present, and this impression persisted.

"Did you get any others?" she asked.

If so, she would ask to read them. In them, no doubt, she would read once more the same promise to come back. But this time it would have its proper date in the past. It would give details placing it in the asylum in Auvergne. It would destroy this dreadful impression that Luc's frenzied message belonged to the present.

But Madame la Hourie shook her head.

"No, they wouldn't let him write to me," she replied. "They only wrote themselves. I begged them, I threatened them; but I never received anything else. He was only able to send this one through a servant, and they dismissed him when they found out. That silence of his! I felt that it would drive me mad. But, as I was saying to you just now, I've been repaid for it. When I read this letter again, it was as though he'd sent it to me from that icy coast, to tell me to expect him. It gave you the same impression, didn't it? As though he'd just scribbled it in haste, on his knee, before starting on his way back."

"Yes," Françoise admitted. She was startled that she should enter so quickly into her deluded mother-in-law's game. "But," she objected, "there was the envelope. There was the post-mark."

"I destroyed it. Of course, there was the envelope. But I destroyed it."

Madame la Hourie laughed, quite satisfied with herself, and it was that haunted laugh of hers which exorcised Françoise.

But during the next few days Luc's mother returned to the charge. As she no longer had anything to hide, either about the past or about her present hope, she talked and talked. For hours on end she overwhelmed Françoise with a flow of miracles. Amid all the wreckage of the *Entreprenant* she picked out one piece, placed her son upon it, and piloted him toward the coast, where the seal-fishers were right on the spot to rescue him. Then she re-hashed Proof Spirit's wretched story. She talked about the sealers' protracted cruises. She refused to realize that such voyages dated back thirty years, before the days of engines and radio.

At first Françoise argued with her, underlining every improbability by refusing to accept it. But Madame la Hourie answered her back. She stressed every syllable with her fore-finger, as though to drive it into her opponent's mind by force.

"Is it impossible? Come on, answer me!"

"I suppose not."

"Well, then . . ."

Françoise gave it up. She contented herself with answering only one bare-faced argument. According to Madame la Hourie, the crew should have sacrificed their own lives to save Luc.

"Captain Halluin was responsible for him. Luc was his owner and his passenger. Necessarily he would have thought

153

about him first. He would have the best boat. It was he that they saved first."

"No, they'd save the cabin-boys first."

Françoise reminded her of this in her quiet voice, and her mother-in-law broke off the conversation with a look of hatred which Françoise felt rather than saw.

That night, after dinner, just as she was going up to her room, Madame la Hourie grasped her by the wrist.

In a very low voice, as though she were entrusting Françoise with a valuable recipe, she said, "Every night, before I go to sleep, I say three times, out loud, 'He's coming back, he's coming back, he's coming back.' Annette is going to say it too. Why shouldn't you, his wife? . . ."

"No, Mamma!"

Why, this was sheer madness! She must escape from it, and at once. Pludual had been right; there was growing danger. The atmosphere around her was changing. It was no longer that of the tomb-prison in which she had been stifled. Her mother-in-law no longer suffocated her with the odor of death. She looked at her with different eyes, eyes that were unbearable. No longer did they see in her Luc's widow; they saw his wife. "You, his wife . . ." Madame la Hourie had just said it.

"Is Monsieur Maurière back?"

An instinct of defense drove Françoise to the telephone. It was the same instinct that had driven her, after her visit to Pludual, to the hospital where Maurière was regaining his strength, his laugh, his refreshing discourtesy. She had asked for the office of the Western Electric Company.

"He should be back tomorrow, Madame. Who is speaking?"

"Would you ask him to call at Plangomeur as soon as he can? This is Madame Françoise la Hourie."

154

"Very good, Madame. Monsieur Maurière will be informed."

"Please take particular note: Madame Françoise la Hourie."

She hung up. She felt freed. He would come, and, keeping nothing back, she would tell him everything: about her childhood at Le Fraô and Hélène's suicide; about her marriage, Luc, her mother-in-law, and this invasion by the dead man. She would tell him, too, about her own hesitation, her own repugnance. This would be the test, this fierce frankness on her part. He must keep nothing back on his side either. Then she would make up her mind.

Early in the afternoon of the next day, she took refuge to await him in the study with its red upholstery. Since the first hot weather in June, she had deserted the drawing room, which faced due south, whereas the study, looking northwest on the woods, was cool and restful to the eyes. Here, during her spare time, she copied for Aunt Angélique extracts from the corsair's log-books, his gallies of crews and prisoners: valuable documents which Mademoiselle de Caradeuc used in her theses for historical societies. Françoise reached for the manuscript on which she was working and started writing.

"Two days later, three large ships arrived as reinforcement for the enemy. Thereupon they made ready on the second day of May, and set sail to blockade us in the bay. But, now that our leaks had been repaired at top speed, I had decided to get out of it by force, dead or alive."

The corsair's vigorous old text had often helped Françoise. A quality both of restraint and strength issued from the thick paper scored by his bold writing.

Françoise finished writing "dead or alive," and then her pen stopped. They were trying to imprison her too. She, too,

155

must get out "by force." She awaited the fight. She foresaw that it would be hard; but she would win it. For it was for her, and not for the enemy, that reinforcements would arrive.

Maurière did not come that afternoon, or the next. The afternoon of the third day, racked with anxiety, dead beat by doubts and suppositions, Françoise telephoned to the Company. There was surprise at the other end of the line. Monsieur Maurière had been given her message two days ago. He had said that he would call at once. Certainly he should have done so. Should he be reminded?

"No, you needn't do that," replied Françoise, sharply. "Perhaps he did come, and I wasn't told. I'll call you back if necessary."

She hung up and rang for Annette, three times. The housekeeper came in, her hard face narrowed by her hair brushed back and sleeked down with water.

"Did no one call to see me yesterday or the day before?" Françoise demanded.

"The engineer came the day before yesterday," replied Annette.

She did not lower her eyes. She waited.

"Well, didn't he ask for me?"

"It was Madame who saw him."

"But it was I for whom he asked?"

"Yes, but it was Madame who saw him."

Françoise brushed past Annette without a word, opened the door, ran up the stairs, and knocked at her mother-in-law's door. Sitting at the window, Madame la Hourie was looking through a gardening catalogue, brightly illustrated. Until now, since Luc's death, she had lost interest in her seasonable ordering of flowers about which she had previously been particular,

156

not to say fussy. She turned down the corner of a page before closing the catalogue.

"Annette tells me that Monsieur Maurière, the electrical engineer, came to see me," said Françoise. "Why wasn't I told?"

"Because you're not going to receive him in your husband's house," replied her mother-in-law.

Françoise stared at her in surprise. Suddenly she found her once more just as she used to be: decisive, steady-eyed, short-spoken.

"It's bad enough already when you are found in the woods together."

So she knew about that, and she had kept silent about it all this time! She had even become capable of holding her tongue again, when it was a question of hurting.

Françoise realized that she could talk to her now as though she were a normal person, and she said, "You know very well you're lying."

Madame la Hourie shook her head.

"No, I'm not lying. Unfortunately. That your conduct is still irreproachable, in the eyes of the world—yes, I'm ready to believe that. But in yourself, in your thoughts, in your desires, are you still an honest woman?"

Françoise took a step toward her.

"What do you mean?"

Then she started, for her mother-in-law seized her by the wrist and pulled her toward her. But she did not succeed in making Françoise's tense body bend.

Keeping her wrist clasped, Madame la Hourie cried, "There's a question to which any honest woman should reply. But you can't answer it. I defy you to answer it. Do you want your husband to come back? Yes or no?"

Her eyes flaming, her head thrown back, she watched her daughter-in-law fiercely. Françoise said nothing. Madame la Hourie flung away the hand she was holding.

"Aha, you see!" she shouted. "Dead or alive? You're given the choice, and you don't say anything. You don't dare to say 'dead,' but that's what you think, you wretch! Isn't that true? Just try to say, 'I want him to be alive.' Not another thing. You won't say it, you *can't* say it. Shame on you!"

Very pale, stressing the terrible word, Françoise replied, "My husband is *dead*. He's been *dead* for more than sixteen months. You refuse to admit it. You insist on thinking he's alive. It's madness, but, out of pity, I haven't said anything. But, now that you're trying to tie me by force to a dead man, I tell you I won't have it. Whether I need my freedom or not, I've every right to take it back. I'm taking it back, and I'm going."

Madame la Hourie leaped out of her chair.

"You're going, eh? And I'll tell you why you're going. You're going to that man who's waiting for you, that man who's driven you to this point. A workman, or next door to it. Just like your sister. The first man who comes along and beckons to you . . ."

"Be quiet!" stammered Françoise, white to the lips.

But Madame la Hourie marched upon her. Her thick lips quivered, and she shook her head so fast that her gray hair, too loosely coiled, started to come down.

"No, you won't make me be quiet. So long as there's a chance, even the slightest chance, that she's still married in the eyes of God, an honest woman, above all a Christian woman, feels bound by that chance. Even the wives of sailors go on hoping. They cling to the tiniest hope. They wait, at least. But you—you refuse to wait any longer. You'd rather run the risk of belonging to two men at once. And you dare to go to church, you dare to take Communion! What do you call that?"

"But he's dead!" Françoise all but shouted.

Madame la Hourie sat down again. All at once, she became appallingly calm. Without even raising her voice, she said, "No, God will bring him back. And I'll keep his wife for him, by force, if necessary. I won't stop at anything. If I have to, on the day that your banns are called, when the priest asks if anyone knows any impediment to your second marriage, I'll stand up, right there in the church, and I'll say, 'Her husband is not dead. Let her prove that he's dead!' And now you can go if you like."

She pointed to the door. Françoise went out. But, once she was outside the room, she stopped beneath the great panoply, as though she thought it was idle to go any farther. Her prison, she felt, had suddenly spread everywhere. Henceforth she would carry it within herself.

"I'LL throw myself in the pond. You'll find everything you want to lay me out in the cupboard there. My papers are in the desk, and the key is in the little vase. The rector won't refuse me burial. He'll understand that you can't stand it all alone, when everyone deserts you. God will understand better still. If you go away, I'll kill myself, I swear to you!"

A harsh voice, lowered almost to a murmur, but cruelly clear through tight lips, replied like an echo, "I'm sure Madame would kill herself."

Annette, standing behind Madame la Hourie's armchair, grasped the back of it. From the other end of the room, beside the big window, Françoise stared at her mother-in-law. At first she tried to see through the frenzied mask of that face raised toward her, in order to distinguish between the element of blackmail and the element of dangerous emotion in her threat. Then she gave it up.

Françoise had just reminded Madame la Hourie, "We fixed Whitsun for my going away, Mamma. I shall be leaving after Whitsun."

That would be in a week.

Immediately, just as a peasant hastily plugs a breach in his hedge with thorn-bushes until he has time to close it properly, her mother-in-law hurled this threat of suicide at her.

Françoise shrank from the effort of trying to decide whether it was serious or not. What did it matter whether she went away or stayed? What did it matter whether she was alone here or elsewhere? Did it even matter so much whether Luc was dead or alive, since this old woman had succeeded in bringing him to life in her?

For the dilemma which her mother-in-law had placed before her with such cruel clarity remained thrust deep into her like a splinter. Did she want her husband to come back? Yes or no? . . . No! She loathed the very thought of it. And why, if not because she wanted another man?

Once she had realized this, Maurière stood condemned. It was because of him that she had committed an execrable crime of intention, which the Church reviled equally with an accomplished crime. It was because of him that she had passionately longed that her husband should indeed be dead. The very next day after her mother-in-law had hurled anathema at her, she had confessed this to herself.

"I accuse myself of wishing that my husband may never come back, so that I may marry someone else."

She still accused herself of it.

One morning, when the mail arrived at ten o'clock, she had had a momentary hope that the monstrous edifice which imprisoned her was about to collapse. Madame la Hourie, her hand trembling, brought her a letter from the Soviet Embassy.

"Open it!" she said. "I can't do it. But be quick!"

Françoise read it in a low voice, but the words rang in her like a fanfare.

"We regret to inform you that we have been unable to obtain any fresh information about the loss of the trawler *Entreprenant*. Investigation carried out in the province of Murmansk has proved that the wreckage found by a Samoyed tribe on the coast of Donka Bay was discovered more than six months after the loss of this ship. Its condition, moreover, showed that it had been a long time in the water. On the other hand, since the date when the ship is believed to have been lost, no ship-wrecked man has been rescued by any Soviet ship or any coast-guard station. With our regrets . . ."

Without a word, Madame la Hourie went up to her room. She got Annette to bring up her meals. This meant that Fran-çoise could not attempt to enter her room.

She resigned herself to waiting to see her mother-in-law in the hall the next morning, when the bell rang for breakfast. Madame la Hourie made her appearance at the turn in the staircase, her short arm following the line of the high baluster.

It may have been because of her weight and her slowness, but Françoise noticed that morning that her mother-in-law knew how to descend the spacious stairs as they should be de-scended, with all the majesty for which they had been built. For a sense of the theatre had dictated their dimensions. They were low enough not to cause an exaggerated bend of the knees, and wide enough to permit a descent which did not disturb any attitude. Madame la Hourie always descended them sol-emnly, even at her most feverish moments. Françoise was struck by this natural nobility of hers.

"Were you able to sleep, Mamma?" she asked.

Once she was in the tiled hall, the old lady turned back into a little old woman, fat and thick-set, agitated by futile move-ments. She shook her head and waved her hands.

"No, I wasn't," she replied. "And I'm very glad I wasn't. They say that the night brings counsel. To us believers"—her voice assumed a confidential tone, almost that of an accom-plice—"that means that it brings grace. It's during the night that you hear best what God wishes to say to you. In the day-time there's too much noise."

She grasped Françoise by the arm and drew her toward the dining room. There, installed at the spacious table, she uncovered the butter-dish and started to butter a slice of bread, with careful little dabs that kept her busily engaged on her job.

"It's always been at night that I've seen most clearly for myself and for other people," she went on. "When I made up my mind to go and ask for you for La Hourie, it was at night. When he had typhoid and I suddenly thought of Professor Boullard, who saved him, it was at night. Of course, it means taking pains, it means tears, it means suffering. You have to pay for everything. My God, what hours I've spent! . . . It was so abominable, that letter. I thought my head was going to burst. And then, all at once, I understood. No, I didn't understand, I *heard*. 'So you trusted the people in Moscow to bring you back your son? You have had their answer. If I restore him to you, you will owe it only to Me.' Oh, what peace it is to do nothing more than have faith in Him!"

She was already crumbling this peace away between her restless fingers. As she spoke of it, her eyes shone. It set her quivering, as though she were awaiting a festival.

Then the novenas started again, secretively. Annette was enrolled every day to carry to the post letters addressed to religious communities and sanctuaries. Requests for Masses and prayers bore as their intention: "For the return of a missing man." Sometimes, in the evening, Françoise caught sight of Annette's birdlike profile, as she sat motionless at her kitchen window, with the lights out. Only her dry lips moved. She was telling her rosary "for poor Monsieur's return."

Françoise, for her part, had to listen to a detailed account of these intercessions, which her mother-in-law classified with joyous, elaborate eagerness, like dividend coupons due for payment. In the end, this weighed upon her so heavily that one morning she tried again to say that she was going away.

163

She spoke about the post of secretary to the archeological society which Aunt Angélique had suggested. Madame la Hourie nearly jumped out of her chair.

"Do you want people to say that I let my daughter-in-law, my son's wife, earn four hundred francs a month by scratching at paper, just like any wretched typist? Do you want them to say that you left here to work?"

The word "work" roused her to indignation—a ladylike indignation which Françoise found it hard to understand. She had, indeed, been brought up to esteem her neighbors, those threadbare aristocrats who recoiled in horror from the very idea of taking a job. She had been taught to appreciate how much true nobility there was in their refusal to do so. She had always been capable of realizing that in their parsimony there was something of the harsh rationing of a besieged fortress, and in their idleness something of the doggedness of leaders who refused to abdicate their position by reducing themselves to the rank of mercenaries. But Madame la Hourie regarded menial work as purely and simply a mark of poverty, and as such it seemed to her to be degrading.

She expounded this at sorry length. It was then, when Françoise refused to give way, when she went so far as to fix a date for her departure, that her mother-in-law suddenly burst out with her threat. If Françoise went away, she would kill herself.

As she said them, the words molded her face into an expression of triumph and defiance so frantic that Françoise weakened. She was not going to play this dangerous game. Madame la Hourie realized the fact. She turned round.

"You may go, Annette."

Without a glance, the housekeeper brushed past the furniture and left the room.

164

As soon as the door closed behind her, Madame la Hourie stood up and went to her desk.

"I didn't want to talk to you about it before her," she said, "but, when I dismissed that—that Maurière, I'd found out something about him. He's been leading a dissolute life at Saint-Malo and at Rennes. He still is. Here, read this!"

She held out a letter.

"No, thank you," replied Françoise.

"But you must! Take it with you!"

She forced the letter into Françoise's hand.

"So you won't even have any regrets. . . ."

The moment she was in the corridor, Françoise tore up the letter, without reading it. "Not even any regrets." She was to be left with nothing at all.

She went out to the garden. At the edge of the big bed, Grioul was leaning over rose-bushes suffering from mildew.

"It's going to make a mess of everything, that nasty stuff," he said, pointing to the moldy leaves. "And that fine fellow Proof Spirit was going to put the sprayer in order, so he said. What he has done is put it out of action. Oh, that fellow! There are plenty of slackers under the sun, but he takes some beating."

Françoise listened to him closely, as though he were saying something important. Her tired brain found it hard to grasp the most trivial conversation.

"Then there's Guéguen, the blacksmith," Grioul went on grumbling. "He was to do the soldering. He doesn't hurry himself either."

He straightened himself, as though he had just remembered something, and glanced at Françoise.

"By the way, there's going to be a wedding."

"A wedding?"

"Yes. The bride's Blanche Toupin, le Barch's daughter, the widow of Toupin of the *Entreprenant*. She's going to marry Guéguen, as it happens. She's my cousin."

He shrugged his shoulders.

"That hasn't stopped her having a taste in advance, as they say. So she's in a bit of a hurry. But, after all, a year and five months—that's more than long enough to wait. Madame hasn't said anything to you about it?"

"No."

"I'm not surprised. But she talked to them all right! She went there and made such a scene with Blanche and her parents. She had only too much to say. It's their business, isn't it, and not hers? So they're not very well pleased."

He cut off some blighted branches with sharp snips of his pruning-shears, and went on, "It's not for me to give you advice. Still, if you have the time to spare, it wouldn't be a bad thing if you went to see the Barchs and told them not to pay too much attention to what Madame said to them. All the more so because she dragged you into it."

"What!"

"She did indeed. She told them that their daughter was a slut to marry again before she was sure her husband was dead. She said that you had wanted to marry again too, but you wouldn't, because you believed that Monsieur might still come back. I ask you!"

As Grioul spoke, he watched Françoise. Like all servants, he was curious about his employers' secrets. Just how much truth was there in what the old woman had said? Was it a question of Maurière, whom he had seen prowling about the park? Or was it a question of Pludual, who chose a day for his visit when he knew the mistress of the house would be away?

166

Françoise met his eyes.

"What people believe or don't believe doesn't make any difference," she said.

She had learned from the peasants to take refuge in evasive sentences like this. Grioul understood.

"You're quite right," he agreed.

He snipped off some more branches.

"But to return to the Barchs," he went on. "It wouldn't have been so bad if they had thought that Madame was talking only on her own account. But, when she told them that you agreed with her too, that's too bad altogether. So, if you went there . . ."

Françoise went that very afternoon. Le Barch, like Minquier, was a fisher of sand-eels. From the end of spring, he and his son took their boat to the Banc des Pourceaux, off Dinard, and swept the shallows with their fine-meshed net, after beating the sea with their oars to drive the shoals of sand-eels into the trap. Françoise arrived at the hour of high tide, in order to find Le Barch at home.

But there was no one at home except his wife, a peasant-woman from Plouër with a narrow face. She watched Françoise come in and did not offer a word of welcome.

"Why haven't you called today, Madame le Barch?" asked Françoise. For the sand-eel fishers never missed Plangomeur on their rounds.

"We won't be calling any more," the woman retorted, raising her fist for emphasis. "And you can see whether you'll get anyone else to supply you."

"But why? What have you got against my mother-in-law?"

Madame le Barch swung round sharply. But she stayed still for a moment, staring at Françoise, before she replied, "What I've got against her is that she came here yesterday and abused

167

us. Shame on her! A woman of her age! She was lucky that le Barch didn't chuck her out of the door. Yes, she was very lucky."

"What was her grievance against you? That your daughter is getting married again?"

"Yes, that she's getting married again. Your mother-in-law wanted her to break off with Guéguen and bring up her baby all by herself. She's been caught, of course, but she's not the only one. Besides, isn't it better that the baby should have a father and something to eat when he arrives? She wasn't so happy with her last husband, either, with his drinking and his knocking her about. We may be poor people, but we're as good any day as people like your mother-in-law, who are no good for anything except making rows."

Françoise tried to make excuses for her: where the *Entreprenant* was concerned, she lost all sense of proportion. But Madame le Barch was not to be disarmed.

"Some people may have the time and the inclination to wait for the dead to come back. They're lucky. But we need our daily bread, and we've got to earn it."

The door opened, and clogs dragged across the beaten earth of the floor. Madame le Barch looked over her shoulder.

"Where have you been?" she asked. "Filling yourself up again and leathering your liver, you wretch!"

The man who had just come in, a broad-shouldered, red-faced man, did not even answer. He looked at Françoise without showing very much surprise, for his cider had made him more human. He dragged a bench polished by backsides from underneath the oak table.

"Let's sit down," he suggested.

His wife shot him a glance of fury.

"And what about your potatoes?" she asked. "Have you

hoed them? Have you hoed them, I say? I suppose I'll have to do them, the same as I do everything else here."

Le Barch winked.

"I haven't had time . . . So it seems that the *Entreprenant's* whole crew are on their way home, eh?"

He had turned toward the visitor and stared at her mockingly, his hands thrust into his pockets.

"Do you know what I think?" he went on. "Well, it's all Proof Spirit's fine work. It's all those stories he's told her that have driven your mother-in-law crazy. He's found a good pantry, that pot-scourer, and he's dishing out the stuff to her. He may not be much of a sailor, but he knows how to swim. When she came here yesterday, screeching like a pulley, I said to her, 'Look here, Madame . . .' "

His wife shrugged her shoulders, but le Barch was now well away, waving his hands about.

" 'Look here, Madame,' I said to her, " 'those stories of people turning up again were all very well at one time, in the old days of seafaring. But nowadays, with radio, and cables, and coast-guard stations all over the place, they're finished. Everyone will tell you the same thing.' "

A shower of rain lashed the windows. Le Barch noticed it.

"Go and hoe your potatoes, eh? You'd have liked to see me out in that, wouldn't you?"

The door opened again, but more suddenly this time. Slanting rain came in, and with it a woman in a long blue waterproof cape.

"Filthy weather!" she exclaimed, as she shook herself.

Then she caught sight of the "young lady from the chateau." She flung back her hood. She was a brunette, with short, curly hair and a thick, strong neck. Her prominent eyes hardened as she stared at Françoise.

"Why don't you take off your cape?" said her mother.

The young woman did not stir.

"Do you hear me, Blanche?" her mother repeated. "Take off your cape!"

Blanche unfastened it and threw it on the bench. She was very obviously pregnant.

Without hesitation, her mother dragged her into the conversation.

"We were just talking about the fine compliments you received last evening."

Blanche frowned, and her mouth twisted.

"Were you? Well, if she'd been a bit younger, she'd have gone out of the door again, and quick, too."

Her anger of yesterday rose in her throat again. She planted her fists on her wide hips.

"We don't owe her anything, do we?"

"She didn't mean to be unkind," Françoise protested.

Blanche Toupin took a step forward.

"She didn't mean to be unkind, eh? I suppose she wasn't being unkind when she said, 'He'll come back. He'll come back and take you away from your new husband'? Oh, when she said that, Mother had to hold me back!"

Françoise stared at her. She could see fear in her eyes, that terror which sometimes sweeps a countryside like a storm. Here again her mother-in-law, with her frenzy of a prophetess, had sown the seeds of panic. Since yesterday Blanche, like Françoise herself, had been harried by the thought of someone coming back. But it was not a living man that Blanche feared. It was a dead man, a man indeed dead, a dead man who came back. She was quite sure that Toupin was drowned. For that matter, she was forearmed against the return of a living Tou-

170

pin. If he came back, he would find her married again, with a baby in her arms, and he would take himself off. It was against the dead man that she was defenseless, against the posthumous jealousy of a dead husband, a stubborn Breton husband, who came back.

She hid her fear so badly that Françoise mocked at herself for coming. The moment Grioul had told her about Blanche, she had hastened to seek the encouragement of a rebel, to have a look at this bold young woman who dared to take another man. What she found was a frightened woman who, on her wedding-night, would listen anxiously to every sound and peer at every shadowy shape in the room.

Françoise and Blanche eyed each other. Blanche's mother wiped some glasses, for the visitor seemed to have come to tender apologies, and one might offer her some cider.

"Of course, it's none of our business," she said. "But suppose you wanted to marry again, would that stop you?"

Françoise shuddered, seared by the question. But this time the daughter, suddenly embarrassed and humble, saved her from having to answer.

"What a question to ask! It's not the same thing at all."

Hard-bitten as she was at market, her mother apologized, and then had another go at Françoise.

"I was just supposing, of course. But, in your own opinion, is she in the right?"

She jerked her chin toward her daughter.

"Of course she is," replied Françoise.

Both the mayor and the parish priest would vouch for Blanche Toupin's right. But "right" was so short and simple a way of putting it! Madame le Barch, however, was quite satisfied.

"That's all right," she said. "You must try our cider. It's quite mild. . . . But why did she talk like that, then? It must have been from spite."

Françoise shook her head.

"Oh, no! It was from grief."

Le Barch spat between his feet.

"She's more than three parts gone in the head," he declared.

Still standing up, still chewing the cud of the threats of which she had yesterday been the victim, Blanche gazed at Françoise with shrewd eyes, softened by a hint of sympathy.

"No, she's not mad," she said. "But she's one of those people who have to torment others. You know that perhaps better than anyone else."

172

FRANÇOISE sat up with a start in the
dark. Someone was knocking at her bedroom door.

"What is it?"

She heard the door open a little and fingers grope for the
switch on the wall. The sudden light hurt her eyes.

"Get up, Françoise, quickly!"

Her mother-in-law stood in the doorway, disheveled, bulky
in her brown dressing-gown. The harsh light of the wall-lamp
made havoc of her face. Her flabby cheeks hung in limp bags,
the whitish skin of her skull showed through her thin hair, her
worn eyelids were red-rimmed. But a restless flame flickered
in her eyes, a frantic expectation moved her lips even before
she spoke.

"There's someone walking round the house."

"We must call Grioul."

Madame la Hourie shrugged her shoulders impatiently,
over and over again.

"No, no! Come on! Hurry up!"

Françoise did not attempt to argue. She felt that she was
becoming more dangerously docile every day. She put on a
wrap, slipped her bare feet into her shoes, and followed her
mother-in-law. In the long corridor the arms gleamed bluish
in the moonlight.

They descended the great oak staircase, crossed the hall,
and went out on to the steps. Before them the long drive plunged
pallid into the dark, rustling trees. The shadows of their

173

branches made black eddies on its surface. Madame la Hourie pointed to the right.

"It was this way," she said.

Françoise let herself be led along, still drowsy. She slept like a child, and this was her sole sanctuary. She took refuge in it at night as one goes home for shelter. She was hard to rouse from it. More than uneasiness, what finally awakened her was surprise: surprise at seeing her mother-in-law walking in front of her with a supple swing very unexpected from her clumsy body. Her head, with its thin hair, turned from side to side in rapid little jerks. Her eyes were on the watch, her ears intent upon all the noises of the night.

They skirted the right wing. At the corner of the house, the old woman suddenly came to a halt. She seized Françoise by the wrist.

"Listen!"

Françoise could hear nothing but the steady murmur of the wind in the leaves, though she listened her hardest.

"I'm sure someone was walking on the gravel just now, right under my window," declared Madame la Hourie.

They walked all round the house. The kitchen-garden, with its bluish plants and its commonplace walls, was empty. So were the path which led round the left wing and the spacious lawn, like velvet in the dark.

"There isn't anything," said Françoise, just as they were getting back to the steps.

"I'm sure there was someone walking about," repeated Madame la Hourie.

Suddenly a window was flung open above their heads, right at the top of the house, and a white form leaned out. It was made up of three blurs: that of a linen nightcap, then a gray

174

blur which was its face, and lastly the white blur of its night-dress.

"What's the matter?" Annette demanded from up there. Their voices had awakened her.

"Didn't you hear someone walking about, Annette?" asked Madame la Hourie.

"No. Shall I let the dog out?"

"Of course not!"

Madame la Hourie shouted it impatiently. Then, as Annette, her suspicions aroused, remained leaning out of the window and scanned the park in her turn, she said, in that tone of annoyance appropriate when some bungler has spoilt everything, "It's not worth while now. Let's go in."

"If there had been anyone," Françoise pointed out, "the dogs would have barked."

Her mother-in-law seized her arm again and squeezed it.

"But suppose it were someone belonging to the house?" she murmured in a tone of frenzied faith. "I heard someone walking about. It was like someone hesitating, someone waiting. Yet they didn't bark. They wouldn't bark, if *he* came back at night like this. And *he* wouldn't ring, for fear of upsetting us too much. He'd walk away again through the park, and not come back till the morning."

From the door, she pointed to the bright drive along which the traveler had disappeared.

Dazed, Françoise stared at the dark hole into which the luminous ribbon of the drive plunged. Suddenly she was conscious of a presence there. Luc was no longer a dead man. For weeks she had defended herself, just as a healthy organism defends itself in an infected environment. But now the last barrier was broken. The contagion had spread to her in her turn.

She *felt* that Luc was alive. She accepted the fact that he had come to the foot of the steps. She lost her head.

"Shall we go down to the end of the drive?" she suggested

Madame la Hourie stared at her in the dark. She seemed scarcely surprised at her surrender, but she shook her head

"No. It's not time yet. He'll come back at his own time, at God's appointed time. And he won't be long, now that there are two of us who know that he's alive."

Françoise shivered, and she added, "Get back to bed quickly, or you'll catch cold."

Back in her room, Françoise closed the curtains, and switched on the ceiling-light and all the wall-lights, so that not a corner should be left in shadow.

"Come, come," she said aloud, "this is not possible!"

It was not about Luc's return that she was thinking. It was about the collapse of her inner strength, which had just given way completely. She had felt a sudden void, and then the conviction that Luc was alive, that he was coming. It had all but made her cry out.

Walking up and down her room, a mannish habit of hers, she tried to assemble rational arguments: nearly seventeen months, the legal declaration of death, the letter from the Soviet Embassy, Blanche Toupin's remarriage. But all this seemed paltry in comparison with that sense of a presence which had stifled her in the garden. Luc was alive. She knew it now with that sureness of intuition which comes from the depths of the soul. She was as conscious of Luc's life as she was of her own.

Still, despite her panic, her outraged reason refused to yield. It protested that everything was just the same. An impression, a feeling, could not affect the past. There was in-

176

finitely less chance of Luc's return today than there had been a year earlier, when, like everyone else, she had been sure that he was dead.

It was all in vain. She watched herself struggling with the chilling certainty that the struggle was futile. For she had undergone that strange doubling of herself at which she used to play in front of her mirror. With pity, but without hope, that part of her which believed watched that part of her which refused to believe. It would give way. Its protests were already becoming faint.

As she walked up and down, Françoise came beneath Luc's portrait. She raised her head. Was she looking at a dead man or a living man?

Stiff in his pose, his eyes staring at nothing, Luc refused to answer her. He avoided her gaze, just as he used to do until, in exasperation, she demanded that he should look at her.

Then, bent on testing the power of words in her turn, she said aloud, "My husband!"

The words set her trembling, as though he had just come into the room. They brought him to life worse than ever. He walked toward her, smiling as he used to smile at night—that dreadful smile of his which merely raised one side of his mouth. She imagined she could feel his hated touch. That set her thinking, just as she used to do, "I'm stronger than he is. I could stop him, if I chose."

So be it! Let him come back, but he would not get her back! She could keep him away better alive than dead.

She stood on a chair, took down the portrait, and thrust it into a drawer, its face to the back. She locked the drawer. Then she thought she could sleep, and she went to bed.

Before she fell asleep, she marshalled the nightmares she

might fear. Thus anticipated, they would lose some of their power. Luc would open the door of her room and come toward her bed. Or he would spy upon her from a corner, behind a piece of furniture. Tense with dread, her heart thumping against her ribs, she would await the moment when he would come out and she would scream.

What she dreamed was something simpler, something more cruel. She dreamed merely that the loss of the *Entreprenant* had been all a dream, that nothing had been altered in their life together, that nothing would be altered. In the depths of her dream lay a dreadful disappointment. She *knew* that, when she awoke, once again she would find Luc's body beside her, flabbier than ever at this hour of the morning. Once again she would feel his mawkish lips against her own. Then there would be the daily business of saying good morning; there would be the mother's greedy kissing of her son, kisses that seized upon his cheeks with a sound like swallowing, while her stumpy arms rested on his shoulders, like elbows on a table; there would be her tight-lipped peck of a kiss for Françoise afterward. Finally, there would be the kiss which Françoise would have to give her mother-in-law on her forehead, flush with her white hair, for fortunately Françoise was the taller.

When she went down to breakfast, scarcely recovered from her night's distress, Madame la Hourie was waiting for her at the foot of the staircase.

"You're still fighting, my dear Françoise," she said. "Oh, yes, you are! Don't tell me you're not! I've been through it. But it's no use. Faith has its way with us, despite ourselves."

"Hope is contagious," Pludual had said. His foresight frightened Françoise now.

During a week of oppressive heat, she writhed like a wounded man on the ground. She had caught this obsession from contact with her mother-in-law. She could cure herself of it only by curing her. She tried. Had she not once exorcised her father when he was haunted by Hélène's unworthy ghost? Of her own accord, she returned to the atlas, to calculations of days and months, to Proof Spirit's stories. She rehashed arguments.

"Look, Mamma, when you think it out . . ."

But their weapons had changed hands. Now it was Madame la Hourie who listened to her with the patient, polite indifference which she had once shown toward her mother-in-law's efforts to convert her. Sometimes Madame la Hourie stressed the futility of her struggle against miracle with a sympathetic smile, half-pitiful, half-mocking. But, untouchable in her own faith, she never answered back, never argued.

Or she might say, "I can hear him coming."

Then Françoise, struck by the thought, had nothing more to say. She was a Breton, and her family, and she herself, had believed in omens, in presentiments, in second-sight. In the end, the old woman's calm certainty got the better of her.

Still, sometimes she had crazy ideas about freeing herself. There were ships, like the famous *Artiglio*, whose job it was to raise wrecks, or at least lower divers into the depths to identify them. If only she could send one to Donka Bay! The diver would see the *Entreprenant* at the bottom of the sea. Among the convulsed corpses he would find one with a big gold signet-ring on its finger, bearing the interlaced initials "L. H." He would bring it back by way of proof. Here it was! Half-hypnotized by her longing, Françoise had to restrain herself from stretching out her hand toward the ring lying on the table.

Often, too, when she looked at the pale map of the Polar Sea in the atlas, which she had pricked with her needle at the spot where the *Entreprenant* had sunk, she dreamed about those Arctic waters, so remarkably clear that one could see wrecks on the bottom.

While she rebelled a score of times a day against her defeat, her mother-in-law dogged her footsteps, uplifted by a hateful gladness. Slowly but steadily, she cleared the house of souvenirs of death, just as she effaced its memory from their daily lives, and put her absent son's belongings back in their place. She was making ready for his return. One evening Françoise found her in her room in front of an open wall-cupboard. She had never known that this secret store existed. Madame la Hourie had covered its doors, on the inside, with all the photos of Luc on which she could lay hands, and on its shelves, with the neatness of an ant, she had arranged all his relics. The bottom of the cupboard was carpeted with neckties. It contained Luc's dressing-case, his first child's spoon and fork, broken toys, his tennis-racquet, and, lying open, his first copybook. His mother was smoothing out neckties and hanging them up, one by one.

As though it were the most natural thing in the world, she said, "I'm beginning to get everything in order again."

The next day, passing behind the drier, Françoise saw shirts and pajamas of her husband's hanging up, which had hitherto been turning yellow in chests of drawers. The sight exasperated her. The madness of this house was by now overflowing outside. Her mother-in-law's mania and her own flaunted itself shamelessly with this linen.

That afternoon, she went to the presbytery, where the rector had asked her to call. Two little girls playing a game stopped her for a moment. They were throwing a ball against a wall,

180

nd Françoise was struck by the artless, heartless ditty with
hich they kept time.

> "Little sheep,
>   Where are you going?
>   To slaughter.
>   What for?
>   To shed my blood.
>   Will you come back?
>   Oh, no, never!"

"Will you come back? Oh no, never!" Françoise repeated
› herself. "Suppose this were a reply?" But no sooner had
he thought it, than she hated herself for having become so
uperstitious that she associated her obsession with everything
at came her way.

At the presbytery, the rector told her that he was planning
› organize a village fair. He had not liked to go to Plango-
eur, or ask for the use of the park, as he had done in previous
ears. In the first place, he had made up his mind too late. So
e would have to improvise and limit the fair to a few stalls.
esides, he knew that Madame la Hourie was very tired, and
e wanted to spare her all the bother. The fair would be held in
e playground of the elementary school. He counted on Fran-
oise as a stall-holder, for this would not be, properly speak-
ng, a fête.

Though she did not say so, Françoise was surprised that,
or the first time, the park at Plangomeur should be abandoned
s the site for the fair. The rector had probably heard that its
wner's mind was wandering, and prudently refrained from
pproaching her. Or had the villagers, at odds with Madame
a Hourie, given him to understand that they would not attend
he fair if it were held at Plangomeur? Françoise did not try

181

to find out. All this mattered so little to her. She agreed to look after a stall, and promised to do her best to explain to her mother-in-law why she was not being asked for the use of her park.

Françoise got home just as the postman arrived. Madame la Hourie was waiting for him in the hall, as she did every evening. She promptly picked out a large envelope from the other letters.

"This is from Canada," she said, in surprise.

"From Canada!"

Françoise repeated it like an echo, and in almost the same tone. They knew no one in Canada, and the same thought had occurred to both of them at the same time.

Madame la Hourie tore the letter open. After reading the first few lines, without going any further she handed it to Françoise.

"It isn't anything."

The letter was from a professor at the university in Montreal, who wanted to know whether there were any documents at Plangomeur dealing with the corsair's visit there in 1703.

"It's not from Canada that he'll come back," Madame la Hourie wound up.

At the foot of the steps, Grioul was laying fresh gravel. He had just received a truck-load.

Madame la Hourie opened the door and shouted at him: "Hurry up! You'll never be ready in time."

She did not say in time for what; but Grioul doubtless understood, for he raked the gravel across the drive furiously.

A kind of truce prevailed at Plangomeur for the next few days. Then, one morning, Françoise saw the housemaids bringing down two long, narrow mattresses from the attic. She recognized them. They belonged to the double bed which she shared with Luc until his departure: two spring-mattresses with two hair-mattresses on top of them, all in one macassar covering. As soon as her husband had sailed, Françoise had had them replaced by a single spring and one mattress. And now the two hair-mattresses were being brought down to be aired.

So her mother-in-law was arranging even for the ghost's nights! Without a word, she was preparing the conjugal bed, making ready to thrust Françoise into it when the time came.

The thought aroused in her a sense of repulsion which she felt was unconquerable. It would yield to nothing: neither to the orders of religion, nor to those of the law, not even to pity. That night, lying in her threatened bed, her nails digging into her palms, she lived again through some of the hateful moments she had spent in it. She remembered frenzied, breathless assaults which Luc had made on her, like a maniac in a hurry. She understood them better since she had learned about his "holiday" in Auvergne. Only once had she got some amusement out of them, when she reflected that in this case he had to act on his own account, without his mother. He had noticed her amusement. He had not dared to ask the reason for it; but she had seen a gleam of positive hatred in his eyes. Was she to contemplate a return to that past? No, she would not!

Little by little, the sheer effrontery of Madame la Hourie's preparations calmed her down. Their attention to detail reassured her. Was this not the very mark of madness? Her mother-in-law was going out of her mind when she put all these petty realities—wool to be loosened, linen to be aired, gravel to be spread—in the place of the phantom hitherto all-powerful. The returning survivor whom she was making up out of her household recipes should be, Françoise realized that night, quite easy to kill.

Next morning, at breakfast, gazing at her mother-in-law with an air of extreme calmness, she asked, "How long shall we wait for him, Mamma?"

Madame la Hourie took refuge behind that nervous little laugh of hers which made her shoulders jump.

"Well, we shan't have to wait for him long."

"But just how long?"

The old woman's laugh broke off. Her eyes shifted from side to side, as though she were seeking some way out. Then she shook her head, as though by way of automatic agreement with herself.

"I can't fix a date for you. But he's coming, he's quite close. I swear to you, my dear, he's quite close. It's just as though I could see him in the distance. He'll be here within the next fortnight."

"Shall we make it a month?"

Françoise made the offer coldly, staring at her mother-in-law all the time, as though she were a dubious debtor to whom she was granting more grace than he asked, but whom she intended afterward to treat relentlessly. Madame la Hourie stared back at her in surprise. Then she looked away again, for she had never seen this resolute look in Françoise's eyes before.

"A month?" she stammered. "What do you mean?"

"I mean that we should wait for him a month more. I mean that, after that, we shouldn't wait for him any more, and that you should agree to this."

This time Madame la Hourie did not turn her eyes away. Brought to bay, she suddenly made a stand.

"A month is longer than necessary."

Françoise shook her head.

"No, we'll make it a month. This is the eleventh of June. Shall we say the eleventh of July?"

184

"If you like."

Silence fell between them. Françoise started her breakfast. She was sure, this time, that she had cut off all retreat for this will-o'-the-wisp of hope which lived beside her and which had evaded her so long.

She had got up this morning with a cold determination, in whose presence nothing counted any more. She was starting a struggle, and she would wage it to the end, with all a Royalist's resolution. She was going to oust this shadow from her life. If her mother-in-law surrendered, so much the better. She would have freed both of them, however cruel the deliverance might be for one. If, as was probable, once the date was past, Luc's mother refused to accept it, if she persisted in going on waiting, it would be the sign of an incurable delusion, which Françoise, for her part, would have nothing more to do than treat with contempt, just as she used to do. For that matter, at the end of the month she would be leaving Plangomeur, after exorcising its phantom. But she was not going to run away till then! As for what would become of that old woman, after she had forcibly wrested her fancy out of her, that was no business of hers. She approached the test with the unconquerable spirit of one of her ancestors making ready for trial by battle.

All day long, Madame la Hourie seemed to prowl around that fixed date. At first it had frightened her, but now it fascinated her more and more, hour by hour.

"During this month, you'll pray with me, won't you, Françoise?" she asked.

"Yes, Mamma."

The next afternoon, she overtook Françoise in the park, all excitement.

"Annette has just given me an idea. Do you know what it is? She said to me, 'Why don't you go to Locronan? The Grande

Troménie is held there on the tenth of July.' We'd agreed to wait till the eleventh, but what does a day matter one way or the other? When she said that, I felt that Saint Ronan had taken our date under his wing. He's a saint of the sea and the islands, you know. There's a stained-glass window of him at Molène. Annette insists that we should go. She believes that those who don't do their Troménie in this world have to do it in the next, and that they can't get any farther every day than the length of their coffins. You've already seen it, haven't you?"

"Yes, with my aunt."

"Quite so. Well, will you agree that, instead of the eleventh, we should make it the tenth, and that we should undertake to do our Troménie together on that day?"

"Very well."

"And on the eleventh, if Saint Ronan has not brought him back to us, I swear to you, my dear Françoise, that I'll go and order his tablet at Bodin's in Saint-Servan."

Madame la Hourie meant the tablet placed in a chapel to the memory of someone lost at sea. She promised it gaily, almost teasingly, like a reward a child will never get for something it cannot do.

"And now," she wound up, "you can't say that I'm not reasonable!"

Françoise nodded assent. What did it matter which saint's protection she chose, so long as he did not help her to escape when the time came to go to Bodin's?

Days went by, and they served only to increase Madame la Hourie's happy excitement. Far from worrying about the flight of time, she complained about how slowly it passed. The miracle had been settled for the tenth, and she made ready for it feverishly.

186

One evening Blanche Toupin hastened to Plangomeur and asked for Françoise.

"So you've had news?" she demanded, almost beside herself.

"No, we haven't," replied Françoise.

"But your mother-in-law's telling everyone that your husband will be here on the tenth."

Françoise shook her head, and Blanche sighed with relief.

"I thought so! But we're getting married on the fifteenth, and you can imagine what a shock it was. I said to myself, 'Perhaps there is some news, and I'd better go and find out.'"

"No, there's no news at all."

"I see. She just got hold of one of her ideas again. Do you know what I think? The best thing anyone could wish for her is that she should go clean off her head."

Françoise shuddered, for Blanche had just frankly expressed a vague thought which sometimes lurked in the depths of her own mind.

"It is indeed," Blanche persisted, with all her harsh common sense. "She wouldn't be so unhappy, and she'd stop tormenting other people. There are quite mild forms of madness. My sister-in-law has a cousin who's been shut up in Pontorson for the last ten years, ever since the death of her baby daughter. She dresses a doll, undresses it, and puts it to bed. She thinks it's her baby. She's quite happy."

The fair took place on Sunday the third of July. There were sports in the school playground, rabbit-racing, a tent in which boys of the church guild, dressed-up and bedaubed, staged a pantomime, and a few stalls consisting of trestle-tables. Françoise sold woollen goods presented by parishioners. Next to her was a long table, streaming with cider, at which two girls, dressed in Pont-Aven Breton costumes, did a thriving business pouring out bowlfuls.

It was the end of a hot afternoon, and a haze of dust hovered in the air. Biretta on the back of his head, hands thrust into his sash, the rector gossiped with a group of men. Two peasant women talked a few yards away. Their slow conversation reached Françoise's ears.

"Poor child, she fell down on her knees, and tore a big hole in her skirt."

"My boy too! He won't stay quiet for a minute, the young rascal. It's a shame, the way he wears out his clothes."

They broke off to watch a car which was turning in the playground, and the elder of them nodded toward it.

"Look at that, Marie-Rose! Isn't that a fine sight, a car with a pointed backside like that?"

They followed it with their eyes until it had passed out of the gate. Then the one addressed as Marie-Rose said, "It's Thursday, isn't it—not this next one, but the one after—that José Toupin's widow is marrying young Guéguen? She's in a hurry, all right . . ."

Her companion said something in a low voice. She turned round toward Françoise, and the two of them went off together.

"I'll take everything you've got left."

Françoise turned round toward her customer. He had approached her stall from the back, and he was not looking at her wares.

"Everything you've got left," Hervé de Pludual repeated. He held out a five hundred-franc note.

"Shall I reckon it up?" asked Françoise, as she took it. "I'll have some change for you."

"No, don't bother. And don't start packing up, either. I'll

send for the lot. Just take the things off the stall. When people see nothing but the bare boards, they'll know that you're sold out, and we can talk in peace."

As Françoise started folding up her knit wear, Pludual asked, "Is Madame la Hourie all right?"

"Oh, yes," replied Françoise.

Pludual kept on staring at her, with a quiet persistence which annoyed her. Then he shook his head.

"Why don't you trust me?"

Françoise looked up.

"Your mother-in-law came to see me," Pludual went on. "She told me that her son would be back on the tenth, a week from today. Did you know that she'd been to Ploézel?"

"I didn't know she went to see you."

"She came to give me a message for you."

"For me?"

"Yes. She asked me to tell you that Luc la Hourie's stay in a nursing home was due only to nervous exhaustion. It really doesn't seem to be a matter of much importance now. But it is a matter of enormous importance to her, because she wants to prepare you for his return. I promised her I'd tell you, not because I had some 'amends' to make in that direction, as she put it, but because it gave me an opportunity to warn you."

Françoise shrugged her shoulders slightly. How did this concern her? Did he really think he had something to tell her? Then she saw the look of warmth in his eyes, still fixed upon her. He came as an ally, and he was the only one she had ever had. He watched over her from afar, and hastened to her side when there was danger. She held out her hand.

"Thank you," she said.

Pludual held her hand in his as he went on, "Don't reverse the roles! You have given me back, if not a reason for living, at least a taste for trying. When I try to protect you, to help you, it's still selfishness on my part. I felt that very clearly, when your mother-in-law came to see me. By the way, why this date: the tenth? She didn't tell me, and I didn't ask her. It would have served only to strengthen her obsession."

"It was my doing," Françoise replied. "In order to be done with it, I asked her to fix a date, after which she'd stop waiting. We chose the tenth because that's the day of the Troménie."

"It was you!" exclaimed Pludual. "But don't you realize that's extremely dangerous?"

Françoise looked at him in surprise.

"How do you mean, dangerous?"

"Why, because her disappointment will strike back like a boomerang, and you're not dealing with a very steady head."

"You're making too much of it," replied Françoise, coldly. She was firmly resolved not to let herself be imposed upon by this new blackmail of madness. Her mother-in-law gave her every day only too many proofs of her spite; she had for months past displayed only too cruel a cleverness in torment-ing her, for Françoise to believe that she was likely to go out of her mind.

"It's the only way to stop this waiting," she declared. "It's preying upon her, and it's become unbearable."

Pludual rested his hands on the bare boards of the table and leaned forward, speaking close to her face, in a very low voice.

"Listen. I can say this to you, indeed I must say it, and you'll know why. I myself fought for more than a year against mad-ness. I had the terrible sensation of feeling my reason dwind-ling within me, thinning away until it was no more than a film ready to be torn apart. I defended myself against dreadful obsessions. I defended myself . . . No, *she* defended me.

190

For, whatever vile people may have dared to say, that child was a saint. She helped me to achieve resignation. She—and you. When I met you, I was at the end of my strength. And then you came, so like her and yet so different, and, above all, so intensely alive. Life came back with you. It would go away again if you went away. So, now when I feel that you're in danger, when . . ."

"Well, my dear Monsieur Hervé, it was a great success, wasn't it?"

Pludual turned round sharply. Then he recognized the priest, and replied with all his usual courtesy.

"A very great success, and I'm delighted to congratulate you on it, Rector."

"It was all due to the efforts of these ladies."

They chatted for a few minutes. Then Pludual bowed before taking his leave.

"Please accept all my congratulations again, Rector. It was a charming fête."

He turned toward Françoise.

"Madame, would you be good enough to convey my respectful compliments to Madame la Hourie? As for what we were talking about just now, on thinking it over I am sure you are right. You have taken the only way to reach a decision. In any case, count on me, whatever happens. I shall be only too glad if you will."

Françoise held out her hand. Pludual raised it to his lips. Then he said, so low that only she could hear, "Don't change your plan in any way, and, whatever happens, remember that I agree with it."

Françoise noticed the firmness with which he stressed his last words. She saw, too, how his fine features had suddenly hardened.

As SHE got out of the car first, to give her hand to Madame la Hourie, Françoise looked around her and recognized the place which had once enchanted her.

She had come to Locronan, for the last Grande Troménie, six years earlier, for it was only every six years that the Troménie, corrupted from the Breton "Tro-Minihy," meaning "Tour of the Monastery," repeated the long round which the hermit Saint Ronan made every six days, up hill and down dale, barefoot and fasting, in a spirit of penitence.

She had then accompanied Aunt Angélique, for at that time Mademoiselle de Caradeuc had suddenly made up her mind to take part in all the traditional pilgrimages, threatened by throngs of tourists, the men in plus fours, the women with scarlet nails.

"Since they're turning into beach parties," she said, "let's at least have a few pilgrims here and there who have some idea what it's all about."

This enabled her, into the bargain, to make a charge or two against the great saints of Lower Brittany, such as Saint Corentin, Saint Guénolé, and Saint Cornély, and to attack them on their own ground, just as in her own district she gave a hard time to Saint Malo, Saint Brieuc, Saint Lunaire, and Saint Suliac, not to speak of minor saints such as Saint Denoual and Saint Goueno.

So she had taken Françoise in June to Notre-Dame-de-Tout

Remède at Rumengol. One Sunday late in August they had paid a visit to Sainte-Anne-la-Palud, with its beach of white sand, raucous with the cries of seagulls and the gossip of tatterdemalions. Françoise had also prayed at Le Folgoët, in the old collegiate church, with its granite ornamented by sculptors in a fine frenzy.

At that time Locronan had meant no more than somewhere to go on Sunday, and its Troménie no more than a curiosity. Just as today, when she got out of the car, Françoise had marveled at the harmony of the mullioned houses, with their carved dormer windows, built by the weavers of the India Company. There was a well with a fine framework of wrought-iron in the village square, and, when one turned round, the square tower of the church, with its slate helm, soared in calm might behind a pointed porch big enough for a cathedral. The whole setting presented an aspect at once smiling and rugged: that of Renaissance work in Brittany, where ornamentation intended for more easily worked stone had to adapt itself to the requirements of granite.

On her earlier visit, Françoise had not taken part in the exhausting procession which wound in slow circuits over a distance of thirteen kilometers. She had waited for it, sitting on top of the hill which it had to climb. Today she had come to make its hard journey all the way. Until its last minute, this day belonged to her vow.

But at midnight, once she and her mother-in-law were back at Plangomeur, she would be able to say, "You see, nothing has happened. Nothing could have happened." She would say it, above all, for herself, by way of marking, once and for all, the end of a childish terror of which she was now almost ashamed. After that, life would go on again, if you could call it "life," that succession of dreary days, from which all she could hope was that in the end they would wear out that stubborn youth whose threat she could always feel within her.

Yet it was to regain this icy peace that today she had brought to Locronan someone who would pay the highest price for it, and brought her almost by force. For, as the last days had gone by, bringing nearer the limit which she herself had set, her mother-in-law's frenzied certainty had fallen to pieces. On the very eve of their departure she had shrunk in terror from the date and begged for delay. But Françoise had brought her back to the fence. To force her to keep her promise, she had found a word which seemed frank and straightforward, but which, she knew, she should never have used to this woman poisoned with doubts, who for months past had spent her time striking a balance between prayers and graces.

"Your promise is *recorded* in Heaven, Mamma."

Recorded! Madame la Hourie had an acute sense of keeping engagements. Her farm leases for payment in kind were worked out to decimal points in order to leave no loophole. She had felt the full force of that word "recorded." Suppose, because she failed to keep her word, God should withdraw Luc's return, after already granting it? Her mind, working day and night at a tormenting trial-balance sheet, labored long over this point. Perhaps, before granting the miracle, Providence was waiting until she had kept her promise in full. It was this thought alone which had dragged her to Locronan.

The four clocks of the tower pointed to three o'clock, and the procession set out from Le Pénity.

Françoise watched the famous Troménie drums pass by, in their sheaths of black velvet and blue cloth, then the choir, then the banners clasped half-way up their shafts by brawny fellows, each with a substitute beside him. These men stared

194

at her, as they would stare at everything that came their way, for it was none of their business to discipline their eyes or keep them to themselves. It was their muscles that were going to pray all along the hard route. What they owed the saint was their strength and their sweat.

Women followed them: the usual pilgrimage crowd, dressed in black. After them came Breton women in white, surrounding a litter bearing a smiling Blessed Virgin. Those who carried it wore their striking wedding costumes. They were buxom wenches in white cotton gloves, white silk aprons strewn with embroidered spangles, and puckered caps, whose ribbons formed a yoke of lace streaming over their shoulders. Their velvet bodices were almost hidden beneath the tinsel embroideries that stiffened them, and, when they had passed, their broad backs displayed golden flowers fashioned like star-fish.

Next came a Gothic reliquary from which sounded a high-pitched, cracked clatter: the hermit's brass bell, made of two sheets of metal roughly riveted together. Its persistent, importunate ringing, as its bearers stumbled along with it, was to go on for the next four hours.

Françoise and her mother-in-law let it pass. Then they joined the procession, along with other women wearing hats, behind a party of Boy Scouts with their white sticks.

They passed along a narrow street. Men jeered at them from the door of an inn, and, behind them, a woman cried out—the short, sharp squeal of someone being tickled.

The pace of the procession suddenly quickened, and, in the rush, its cohesion was lost. Then an abrupt halt welded it together again. It had reached the end of the little town. Here, on the right, stood a low hut. Beneath the sheet which formed its roof, a bell rang. It was an old man who rang it, sitting in his green arbor, side by side with a tall stone statue. Forty-four saints' huts were spaced out along the route. Saint Roch, the oldest, had the first of them. Madame la Hourie stepped aside to put a banknote in his plate.

She did the same for Saint Mathurin, in his black chasuble, for Notre-Dame du Rosaire, for Saint Sébastian, for Saint Joseph, for Saint Marguerite, and for Saint Herbot, the six other spectators who lined the route as far as the road to Chatoulin.

Here there was another halt for Saint Eutrope. A priest exhibited a reliquary-casket. The custodian offered glasses of water from a fountain in which the relics had been plunged. The sun was making the tarred road soft. Beside it two Algerian trinket-sellers looked on. Beneath a red tent, a gipsy woman with greasy ringlets and earrings shifted rings at twenty sous apiece about in a trayful of sawdust.

There were two other halts: one for the Ecce Homo, his hands bound with a sailor's half-hitch, the other for Saint Germain d'Auxerre. Then the procession set off on its heroic round. It was heralded by a faster beating of the drums at the head, like the sounding of a charge. Henceforth the Troménie left made roads behind. Following the footsteps of the saint, it would jolt across heaths, bury itself in cart-tracks, be bogged in marshes. In the fields, swaths of clover or corn had been cut for it, lest it should stray from its hallowed route. Gaps had been made in briar hedges, walls had been knocked down, doors had been thrown by way of bridges across reed-grown swamps. The procession became a long file of ants which nothing could turn aside from their chosen path.

Clouds of dust rose beneath the pilgrims' feet. The chanting of the choir and the priests away at the head forced the pace. All at once the Troménie assumed the nature of a sweating, breathless struggle.

It began with a heath blasted by heat, a heath with low gorse-bushes, like bristling hedgehogs rolled into balls, which scratched the women's ankles through their stockings. Here the music of the fervent athletes sounded hoarser in the streaming sunshine. Then the procession strung out along a narrow path, at whose end there was a momentary glimpse of a black cape jutting into a patch of molten sea. Banners wrestled with briars, while others went forward slanting sideways.

Now the procession was advancing in single file, and Françoise turned round to wait for her mother-in-law. She found her right at her heels, already all gray with dust, bending forward and breathlessly clicking her rosary.

In front and behind, banners and golden crosses pitched and tossed, or came to a halt before attacking the thickets, and above the harsh chanting their bearers could be heard cursing or laughing as they were caught in the traps of the viburnum. Birds soared from the bushes. Bigoudènes in lace caps like mitres walked bent, with careful little movements of their heads like insects, for fear of catching them.

Pradic-an-Droviny—a stretch of reeds, with hollows full of yellow water. Some faggots of brushwood had been flung down to form a causeway, but they had already sunk into the mud. Some of the young men hesitated, and then climbed up the bank. But, with no such cheating, the Breton girls in their white shoes who carried the Virgin's litter strode into the slime up to their ankles. Françoise followed them, and, after a few careful steps on patches of dry ground, she too sank over her low shoes, and felt the cold grip of the clay. She turned round again. Her mother-in-law was behind her, hobbling through the soggy ground, her stockings plastered with mud.

"Would you like to take my arm?"

Madame le Hourie did not answer her, not so much in order

to observe the absolute silence which was the rule of the Troménie for women, as because she had ceased to hear anything, so absorbed was she in her fearful hope. Uneasy about her, Françoise slowed down to stay beside her.

"You're very tired, Mamma," she persisted.

This time, Madame la Hourie made a face, and then shook her head in annoyance, as though she were driving a fly away.

Emerging from the swamp, the procession reached a burning stretch of fields, their soil soft and dry, from which rose a haze of dust.

"God, I'm thirsty!" swore a standard-bearer.

"And my throat's skinned," declared his substitute, walking beside him.

Surpliced priests flanked the procession. Suddenly, reading from their breviaries, they struck up a hoarse chant which, starting at the head of the Troménie, was taken up along its ranks—the hymn of Saint Ronan. In Breton, it sang the praises and the prodigies of the old Celtic saint, fierce in his inspiration, powerful over the elements, tamer of wolves and shrews. Then the trumpets heralded the entrance to the Roman road. From there, on the side of the hill, Locronan could be seen, its granite gray as ever despite the sunshine. Next the procession plunged into a shady avenue of chestnuts, all too short, in which Saint Laurent presented his gridiron and Saint Barbe her tower. At every halt, Madame la Hourie, still seeming in a dream, stepped aside to put a ten-franc note in the plate.

Saint Milliau, Saint Jean l'Evangéliste, Saint Guénolé . . . Thirteenth, fourteenth, fifteenth halts: short pauses beside the white huts, which added the fatigue of standing still to that of the painfully slow march. By now the procession had been tramping for two hours, plunging deeper into the heart of the torrid countryside. At every fountain that presented itself at a turn in a sunken road, at every well encountered on the way through a hamlet, the Troménie disbanded. The men made a rush for the water, jostling one another around it, lapping it up noisily in the hollows of their hands. Then they hurried back, wiping their mouths on the cuffs of their sleeves, and took up their places again around their banners.

At Guernevez, a hamlet in a clump of old trees, there was cider to be had. The villagers stood in their doorways offering it in basins and cauldrons. Crosses and standards changed hands hastily, and their bearers made another rush. Bowls were filled and refilled. They swallowed them at a draught, shouted "Thanks!" and set off again, head down, red in the face. Their sweat dripped on to the road.

Françoise looked up. The mass of a hill bristling with black gorse-bushes rose ahead of the gold crosses. On its crest, a sprinkling of sightseers awaited the epic climb. This was Plac-ar-c'horn, "the place where the horn fell." It was here that a virago, an enemy of the saint, with a blow of a beater broke a horn of one of the oxen harnessed to his hearse.

Emerging from a sunken path, as though out of a trap, the head of the procession crossed the road to Chateaulin again, and the stiff climb began. The drums beat with all the frenzy of an assault. By now the whole Troménie was in shirt-sleeves, coats off, necks bared. Faces were barbarously tattooed by dust streaked with sweat. Here was the sternest test in the penitential round, and the adjuration which burst out at the first steps of the ascent bore witness to its significance as an expiation:

"Parce Domine, parce populo tuo!"

The right thing to do was to take no notice of the slope, to carry the banners as erect as possible, to raise the crosses as high as possible. Nevertheless, this Breton hill rose all of a sudden, just as one wave lifts another. The dry grass was slippery, trampled ferns made slides, but the climb went on. As the girls bearing the Virgin's litter clambered up, those in front bent right over, carrying the shafts sheathed in blue velvet almost flush with the ground, so that the statue should stand up nobly, without leaning back. Holiday-makers and journalists stepped backward, taking photos. Women in light dresses and sun-glasses fringed the climb of the unyielding procession.

One of the standard-bearers shouted at them, "We're killing ourselves, and what for?"

The Parisian women laughed, not so much at what he said as at his rough accent and his stumbling.

"For the sake of Heaven!" retorted a curate.

A cross-bearer slipped and fell on his knees. Another man caught the cross and climbed on. The hermit's cracked bell, in its gilded turret, seemed to take possession of space as it rose higher. Its persistent quavering note became a presence which, better than the trumpets, fired the hearts of the climbers. The saint's bell urged them on, like a sheep-dog rounding up a flock. The bearers made headway only step by step, grimacing, sagging at the knees, but they kept their banners soaring upright. Old men hoisted themselves up bent double, clasping their rosaries in both hands as though they were hauling them along. Old women, their heads bowed beneath their white caps, paid no heed to anything, the slope, the gaping spectators, or the click of cameras. They climbed only for their sins, toward that Heaven which would wipe them away.

Haggard, her thick lips drawn with exhaustion, dragging herself along, Madame la Hourie climbed to find her son at the top. Françoise could see her toiling, but now she did not venture to offer her aid in scaling her chosen calvary. Breton respect for the integrity of a vow had seized hold upon her again. Her mother-in-law must win or lose alone.

Beside her, others, at the end of their strength, collapsed in the heather. One of them slid down the slope, his legs pawing the air like a donkey having a roll, and then came to a stop, wedged against a clump of gorse, and stayed there. People laughed and went on. What had knocked him out: sunstroke or cider?

"Come on, come on!"

The clergy rallied the assault. The heather sprained sandaled feet. A thin bearer showed his teeth with the strain of his effort. The spectators who had gathered from the bathing beaches were dumbfounded at the sight of the pilgrims. They felt that this climb was beyond them, that understanding of it was denied them. Their jeers stuck in their throats, and they found them as hard to swallow as fishbones.

At last the crest was reached. Banners were leaned against the walls of the chapel, and the bearers sank down at their feet. A priest made his appearance in the granite pulpit. "In the name of the Father, and of the Son, and of the Holy Ghost . . ." People listened to him standing or sitting—even sitting in tents where cider was served.

"Sit down a little, Mamma," urged Françoise.

This was permitted and did not break the rules of the Troménie. Other people had sat down in the heather. But Madame la Hourie refused. She did so in an odd, mechanical way.

"No! No! No! No!"

Françoise gave it up. Fatigue and the heat suddenly overwhelmed her too. All she had dragged along the route of the Troménie was emptiness of soul. She had followed it with her mouth full of dust bitter as ashes. Her chemise clung to her back with cold sweat. Her burning eyes, searching in the distance for repose, rested on the square fields, the milky water of Douarnenez Bay, the steep rise of the Menez-Hom.

She had just walked through those fields, beneath those trees. They had reverted to silence, to the stillness of the countryside, and the sun, already past its zenith, spread over them the melancholy of plains from which the light is slowly withdrawing. The emptiness of the horizon invaded her like a cold breeze. She turned round and looked to her left, toward the thronged plateau. In a car close by a man and a girl were sitting still, arms around each other, cheek to cheek.

The sight clutched at Françoise's heart. Then reason came to her rescue. Did she want to be sitting side by side with Maurière like that? No! It might have sufficed for a few hours, but it would have brought her only a different kind of loneliness, worse than the one that gripped her now. She knew that today. Had she not always known it? What her mother-in-law had stolen from her was something very different from his caresses. She had sterilized her life; she had seized upon her self-sacrifice, for the sake of a shade. Françoise had been generous once, but she was not generous any more. Otherwise, would she have dragged this unhappy woman, standing bent-backed before her, up this hill? Would she have killed her dead son for her?

The priest in his stone pulpit stopped speaking, and made a spacious sign of the cross. The Troménie, suspended for a few minutes, set off again. Madame la Hourie stumbled heavily over a stone. Françoise took her by the arm. From behind, other people pushed them forward.

They made their way along the crest of the hill, and then descended it to the west, toward the sun which hung in the distance over the dazzling sea. The procession was coming to an end.

"Dixit Dominus . . ."

202

Vespers were chanted along the Roman road. At length the porch of Le Pénity, golden with moss, swallowed up the pilgrims. To enter it they passed under the heavy reliquary of the saint, held up at arm's length by its bearers.

Inside the church, greener than a cave with mildew, Madame la Hourie fell on her knees on the flags. When the monstrance was raised, at the blessing of the Holy Sacrament, she prostrated herself, her forehead touching the stone floor. After the *Te Deum*, she got up heavily, propping herself on her hands, like an old woman after a collapse, and Françoise led her outside. They found Grioul waiting beside the car. He had drunk enough to make him drive fast, and Françoise was glad of it. She was in a hurry to escape. They got in and sat down.

"What time is it?" asked Madame la Hourie, her eyes closed.

"Six o'clock, Mamma."

"Shall we be back before midnight?"

"Of course."

The old woman nodded her head repeatedly in approval, and said no more.

Françoise watched the hill of Plac-ar-c'horn vanish and the road open up before them. The fateful day was coming to an end. What a waste of time it had been! Coming all this way to get rid of a fear which now seemed to her as grotesque as a feverish delirium at which one laughs when one is well again! What was she taking away from Locronan? Only the certainty that she was alone.

The car slowed at a cross-road, and Françoise caught sight of three children sitting at the door of a house. The one in the middle, with tousled fair hair and red cheeks turned gooseberry-color with dirt, stuck out his tongue at her.

"I shall never have any children," Françoise said to herself, and her hand gripped the velvet arm-rest.

At Chateaulin, Grioul suggested stopping for dinner. But Madame la Hourie emerged from her prostration to refuse, violently.

"We shall never be back by midnight. We must be back before midnight."

She was breathless with positive panic. She clenched her fist, and it trembled.

"But surely you're not going all day without eating anything, Mamma?" Françoise protested, for she had already refused to have any lunch.

"Yes, I am! Yes, I am!"

Madame la Hourie pointed to her throat.

"In any case, I couldn't swallow anything. My throat is as dry as a bone. There's something in the basket if you want it."

"I'm not hungry either."

"All right, then! Let's get on, let's get on! It's nine o'clock."

Itching to be off, she did not calm down until the car had picked up speed again.

The countryside was already becoming dark. To the south a hill reared its head, its crest like a sand-dune in the desert, accompanied the car for a few moments, and disappeared. At Pleyben the wonderful calvary, standing on its triumphal arch, was by now no more than a gray mass. Night overtook them at Rostrenen, but at Mur-de-Bretagne Lake Guerlédan gleamed for some time to their right in the moonlight.

Her eyes closed, Madame la Hourie seemed to be asleep. Françoise kept on gazing at the dark fields fleeting past outside the glass. That deadened her thoughts. At length she drowsed off.

All at once, she felt herself seized by the arm. She opened

her eyes, and recognized the front door of Plangomeur, white in the glare of the headlights. By now her mother-in-law's stubby fingers were digging into her flesh. She understood, and, with a trace of irritation, she said, "Now, Mamma, pull yourself together."

Grioul stationed himself beside the steps. Madame la Hourie got out of the car heavily. She stopped at the last step, overwhelmed in advance by what awaited her behind the closed door. Françoise took the key from her, opened the door, and switched on the light. Annette appeared at the door of the study. Her rosary made a little clicking sound as she lifted it.

"Well, Annette? . . ."

The old servant stared at Madame la Hourie with her penetrating eyes. When she too realized what miracle, what presence, it was that her mistress had been expecting, she looked down.

Dragging the words out of herself with a dreadful effort, trying to make them sound commonplace, Madame la Hourie asked, "No one has come?"

Annette shook her head.

All alone, huddled up, the old woman walked to the staircase. She stumbled badly at the first step. Annette caught and held her as she fell.

THE August storm covered the whole countryside. You could feel the livid sky suddenly come closer, until it almost touched the treetops. Its weight, this late afternoon, would grow heavier and heavier until it became too much for it, and it burst.

Madame la Hourie was sitting at one of the French windows of the darkening drawing room. She had resumed her watch at this spot from which one could see right down the drive.

On the morrow of the Troménie, without any need for insistence on Françoise's part, she had admitted her defeat. It was all over. She knew that now. It had been all over for nearly eighteen months. Then she had wept for her son, with agonized sobs, as though she had only just lost him.

After that, she clutched Françoise by the arm.

"I'm all alone now. Don't leave me all alone!"

Her appeal was so poignant that Françoise let her take her hands.

She promised to stay with her. She had gone on promising ever since, over and over again every day, because it was impossible for her to escape from her own instinct to help. She was afraid that something might happen to her mother-in-law in her despair. She had to be made to eat. She had to be made to sleep. She had to be given doses of veronal, and then the bottle had to be locked up. An eye had to be kept on the pond.

For that matter, the old woman had become pitifully docile. She contented herself with leaning with all her weight on the nearest arm, and on her household's patience with her. At the same time, she complained that her memory was going, that she could feel her thoughts becoming unraveled and slipping away from her. One day, on their way back from the daily walk which Françoise made her take in the park, she stopped her daughter-in-law.

"I wonder whether I'm going mad," she said.

But she went on to give such definite orders and make such shrewd suggestions about getting her farmers to pay their debts and evading their demands that Françoise was soon reassured.

Françoise entered the drawing room. Madame la Hourie got up and hastened to her. It was for her arrival that she had been watching at the window.

"What a long time you've been!" she exclaimed. "You've been gone for more than an hour, and you hadn't far to go. Didn't you see the storm coming up? Where are you going now? You needn't take your things off yet. Sit down here."

She pointed to an arm-chair beside her. Then she made a face and gestures of annoyance with her left arm.

"It's stifling," she lamented.

It was indeed. Despite the open windows, the air was so inert that it did not enter one's mouth freely. It was as though it had to be sucked in when it reached the lips.

At the first peal of thunder, though she did not stir, Madame la Hourie gave a short cry, a kind of hoarse bark. It made Françoise jump.

"Why, Mamma," she asked, "surely you're not afraid of the storm?"

She had never been afraid of storms. She had always refused to have a lightning-conductor on Plangomeur. The trees, she declared, were enough protection.

"But of course not!" she replied, almost shouting. Then she

207

started laughing, loud and long, as though the question had amused her. Suddenly on the alert, Françoise stared at her.

Madame la Hourie pointed at her. In a tone like a little girl's at school, she said, "It's she who's afraid! It's she!"

At the second flash of lightning, she jumped as though electrocuted, making a face as though she were in pain. But, after the rending sound of the thunder, she raised a finger.

"I wasn't afraid that time. I wasn't afraid, was I?"

"Of course not."

Françoise was shutting the high windows of the drawing room. Madame le Hourie stood up.

"I'll go and shut the upstairs windows," she said.

"I'll go and do them," said Françoise. "Stay here."

"No. No. No. No."

It was a recent nervous habit of hers, this rhythmical, automatic way of refusing. Françoise thought about it a moment or two. Then a squall which set the two sides of the last window banging and blew in the rep curtains claimed her attention. She hurried to fasten the clasp. Scarcely had she closed it when a flash of lightning splashed fire all over the windows, and a cataract of thunder crashed down upon the park and the house. Immediately after, like an echo of the din, she heard her name shouted from upstairs.

"Françoise!"

She rushed out of the room. At the foot of the staircase, a second shout reached her ears, but this time she could hear that it was full of a superhuman joy.

"Françoise!"

She ran up the broad stairs two at a time. On the landing stood Madame la Hourie, waving her arms, her mouth wide open, transfigured by a dreadful delight.

"He's here!" she stammered.

"Here!"

Françoise echoed it with terror of a miracle clutching at her heart. The joy of this woman trembling in front of her was so intense that it swept everything before it.

"Yes, he's here, he's here!"

Her mother-in-law pointed to a closed door.

"He's just gone into his room."

Françoise ran to it. But her rush stopped dead at that closed door. She stood for a moment, holding onto the knob, her legs giving way under her, her breath coming short. Then, with a shake of her shoulders, she pulled herself together. She flung the door wide open, so that it banged against the wall. The room was empty.

She stared into it for a few seconds, long enough for her eyes to return to reality. Then she turned round.

"But there's no one here, dear Mamma," she said. "Look for yourself."

Madame la Hourie came in, looked all round the room, and returned to the door.

"He went when he saw you!" she cried.

A flash of lightning reddened the corridor. It set the steel of a panoply ablaze. As though drawn by a magnet, the madwoman leaped toward it, snatched a boarding-axe from its hooks, and brandished it in the air. Françoise simply stepped aside. The weapon sank into the paneling. Only then did Françoise shout, "Annette!"

"Indeed, it would be kinder if you went away than if you stayed. When you're not there, she sees her son, she talks to him. She stays quite quiet. When she sees you, she thinks he's gone away because of you, and she goes clean crazy. You know that yourself, since she tried to kill you. She'll try again. Then they'll shut her up at Bégard. But I can manage her all right by myself. I don't mind . . . Well, when are you thinking of going?"

Standing in her kitchen, Annette gazed at Françoise with her gray eyes. Françoise had listened to her without stirring.

"At once," she replied.

"It would really be better for everyone."

The housekeeper wiped her hand on her apron, since she might have to shake hands with Françoise. Then she went on, "Now that you've made up your mind, there's no point in waiting. The girls can pack all your things at leisure, and I'll send them wherever you tell me. . . . You know what she's like. She's upstairs and downstairs all day long. You can hear her shouting even out in the drive. She's like an uneasy spirit, so long as she feels you're here."

Françoise agreed again.

"It's not your fault, what's happened," Annette conceded, disarmed by her submissiveness. "You tried to make her see sense. As for me, old fool that I am, I almost thought . . . Well, what's done is done. So hurry upstairs now and get what you want. I'll look after her meanwhile."

Françoise did as she was told. She went upstairs and filled two suitcases with clothes and underwear. Fearfully, she was careful to make no noise.

Once outside the house, she found Grioul. He took her baggage and carried it to the garage.

"So you're off?" he said. "It's not going to be much fun here, once you've gone. But things can't go on like this. Besides, it's no life for you here now. Where shall I take your trunks?"

"To Rocmarin."

"Oh, yes, to your aunt's. You'll certainly be better off there than here. I'll be seeing you now and again, won't I?"

Françoise nodded, without answering, got into the car, started the engine, and held out her hand through the window.

"And good sailing!" cried the old fisherman.

At the end of the drive, Françoise hesitated which way to turn. Right or left? Right led to Rocmarin, Aunt Angélique, her labeled stones, her tiresome tales, her craze about Serena. Left led nowhere. Françoise turned left.

Almost unconsciously, she took several more turnings along various roads. Then she recognized the way, and slowed down suddenly. She was astounded that she should have come here, without thinking about it. This white road, thick with dust, led straight to Ploézel, to Hervé de Pludual.

Still, she went on driving slowly along it. A storm of conflicting thoughts raged within her. At the end of this road, someone wanted her, someone would welcome her. And he was the one soul in the world who awaited her. She would say to him, "I want a husband. I want a home. I want children." He would understand.

All at once, she stopped the car. Where was she going? Into the first arms held out to her? To promise herself to a man whom she did not love, a man who, for his part, loved her only through the image of a dead woman?

A dead woman! A touch on the gear-lever, a hasty unbraking, and she was off again. She knew now where she was going.

Françoise-Bertrande de Fraô de Lanhéac, daughter of Leaguers and Royalists, was on her way to battle once more. She had just been driven away by a shade. She must take her revenge. Another phantom awaited her at Ploézel, another obsession: the ghost of Cécile whom she resembled. She was going

211

to drive her away, because Cécile had suddenly become her enemy, worse than any living woman. She was going to wrest away from her the man whom she held in her clutches: the man who had warned her, the man who had helped her. Françoise was well used to such struggles. The dead had weighed heavier in her life than the living. The specters of the Rance, Hélène, Luc—they had assailed her more fiercely. She had been all but buried alive with Luc's phantom. She had freed herself. She would free Pludual from his phantom.

She drove faster.

The slow sound of the cracked bell, which she had never forgotten; the rush of the two dogs, their growling flush with the ground, their muzzles sniffing at the dust under the bar of the gate; the gate itself cautiously opening . . .

"It's you!"

Pludual looked at her with bleary eyes, as though he had just awakened. It was Pludual neglectful of his appearance, his face darkened by his beard, his clothes frayed, standing in front of his overgrown flower-beds—Pludual as she had seen him at her first visit. It was Pludual as she had expected to find him.

As they crossed the courtyard, she told him about the crisis which had driven her away from Plangomeur, her mad mother-in-law's attack upon her with an axe. Pludual nodded in understanding, sleepily.

"Yes," he said. "Yes, I felt that you were in danger."

But it was as though he were recalling something in a very distant past.

They reached the foot of the steps. Françoise came to a stop at the first of them, her heart pounding. Would she have the courage to go up them? What awaited her in this house threatened so much to surpass her strength.

212

Standing still beside her, Pludual confessed, "I didn't expect to see you again."

Françoise turned round sharply, as though he had guessed why she had come.

"Why not?"

Everything, she felt, depended now on his answer.

"Because you despise me."

She looked at him. He was obviously a beaten man, but he had been beaten in a struggle whose severity she had just experienced.

"No," she said, "not now."

Resolutely, she walked up the steps. Pludual followed her. He stood aside at the door.

As she passed him, Françoise said, "Before taking refuge with my aunt at Rocmarin, I wanted to talk to you."

Pludual bowed.

On the hall-table lay a pair of woman's gloves. Françoise pushed them aside to put down her own. Pludual opened the door of the drawing room.

"Please come in," he said.

Then, as Françoise entered the room, he stepped back, and swiftly, in two deliberate movements, replaced the dead girl's gloves exactly where they were before.

37232